play guitar with...

21st century rock

Published by
Wise Publications
14-15 Berners Street,
London W1T 3LJ, UK

Exclusive Distributors:
Music Sales Limited
Distribution Centre, Newmarket Road,
Bury St Edmunds, Suffolk IP33 3YB, UK
Music Sales Pty Limited
20 Resolution Drive,
Caringbah, NSW 2229, Australia.

Order No. AM984951
ISBN 1-84609-437-2
This book © Copyright 2006 Wise Publications,
a division of Music Sales Limited.

Compiled by Nick Crispin
Edited by David Weston
Cover designed by Fresh Lemon
Cover photograph (Dave Grohl) Bertrand Guay/AFP/Getty Images
Printed in the EU

Your Guarantee of Quality
As publishers, we strive to produce
every book to the highest commercial standards.
This book has been carefully designed to minimise awkward
page turns and to make playing from it a real pleasure.
Particular care has been given to specifying acid-free,
neutral-sized paper made from pulps which have not been
elemental chlorine bleached. This pulp is from farmed
sustainable forests and was produced with
special regard for the environment.
Throughout, the printing and binding have been planned
to ensure a sturdy, attractive publication which
should give years of enjoyment.
If your copy fails to meet our high standards,
please inform us and we will gladly replace it.

www.musicsales.com

Wise Publications
part of The Music Sales Group
London / New York / Paris / Sydney / Copenhagen / Berlin / Madrid / Tokyo

CD track listing

CD1

Full instrumental performances (with guitar)...

1 **all my life**
(Grohl/Hawkins/Mendel/Shiflett)
EMI Virgin Music Limited/ Universal/MCA Music Limited.

2 **are you gonna be my girl**
(Cester/Muncey) Famous Music Publishing Limited.

3 **bohemian like you**
(Taylor-Taylor) Chrysalis Music Limited.

4 **burn baby burn**
(Wheeler) Universal/Island Music Limited.

5 **come back around**
(Nicholas) Universal Music Publishing Limited.

6 **elevation**
(U2) Blue Mountain Music Limited.

7 **fall to pieces**
(Sorum/McKagan/Weiland/Kushner/Hudson)
Chrysalis Music Limited/Copyright Control.

8 **first date**
(Hoppus/Delonge/Barker) EMI Music Publishing Limited.

9 **go with the flow**
(Homme/Oliveri) Universal Music Publishing Limited.

10 **hysteria**
(Bellamy/Wolstenholme/Howard) Taste Music Limited.

11 **I just don't know what to do with myself**
(David/Bacharach) Universal/MCA Music Limited/
Windswept Music (London) Limited.

12 **lyla**
(Gallagher) Sony/ATV Music Publishing (UK) Limited.

13 **just because**
(Farrell/Navarro/Chaney/Perkins/Ezrin)
Rondor Music (London) Limited.

14 **numb**
(Bennington/Shinoda/Bourdon/Hahn/Delson/Farrell)
Zomba Music Publishers Limited.

15 **red morning light**
(Followill/Followill/Petraglia) Windswept Music (London)
Limited/Universal Music Publishing Limited.

16 **stumble and fall**
(Borrell/Ågren) Sony/ATV Music Publishing (UK) Limited.

17 **somebody told me**
(Flowers/Keuning/Stoermer/Van Nucci)
Universal Music Publishing Limited.

18 **take me out**
(Kapranos/McCarthy) Universal Music Publishing Limited.

19 **talk**
(Berryman/Buckland/Champion/Martin/Hütter/Bartos/Schult)
BMG Music Publishing Limited/EMI Music Publishing
Limited/Warner/Chappell Music Limited/Copyright Control.

20 **vegas two times**
(Jones) Universal Music Publishing Limited.

CD2

1 **tuning notes**

Backing tracks only (without guitar)...

2 **all my life**

3 **are you gonna be my girl**

4 **bohemian like you**

5 **burn baby burn**

6 **come back around**

7 **elevation**

8 **fall to pieces**

9 **first date**

10 **go with the flow**

11 **hysteria**

12 **I just don't know what to do with myself**

13 **lyla**

14 **just because**

15 **numb**

16 **red morning light**

17 **stumble and fall**

18 **somebody told me**

19 **take me out**

20 **talk**

21 **vegas two times**

To remove your CD from the plastic sleeve,
lift the small lip to break the perforations.
Replace the disc after use for convenient storage.

all my life

Words & Music by Dave Grohl, Taylor Hawkins, Nate Mendel & Chris Shiflett

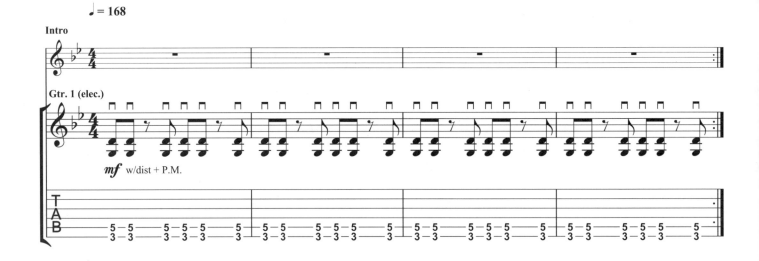

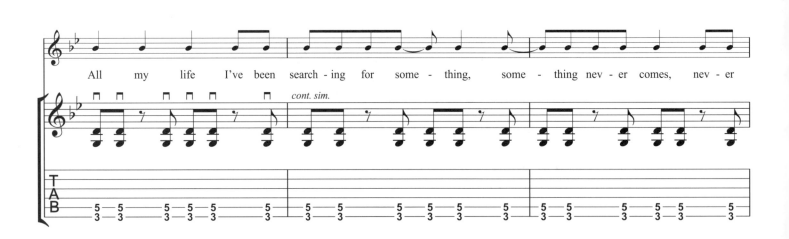

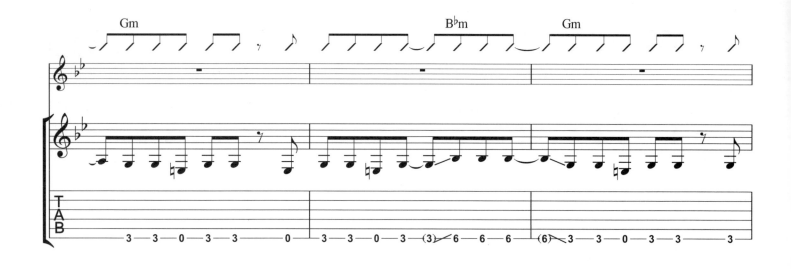

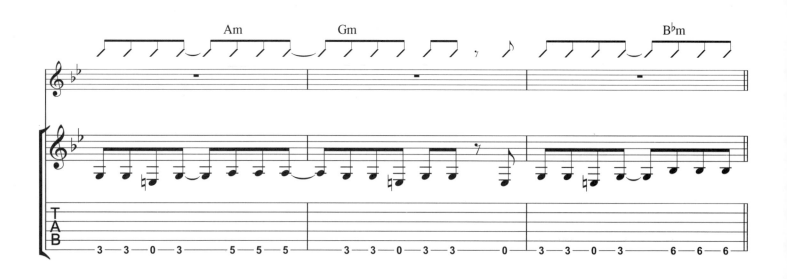

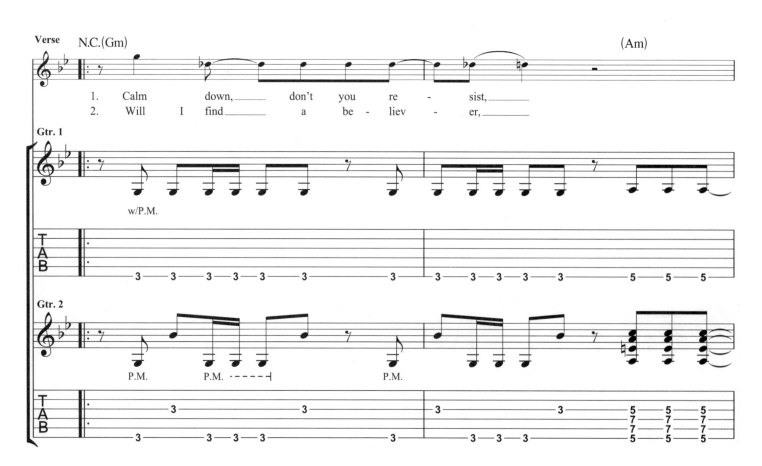

1. Calm down,_____ don't you re - sist,_____
2. Will I find_____ a be - liev - er,_____

Will I find_____ some - thing in there
If I get_____ an - y clos - er

to give me just what I need?_____
and if you o - pen up wide,_____

An - oth - er rea - son to bleed,_____
and if you let me in - side,_____

Bridge G⁵

Gtr. 1

cont. sim.

mf w/P.M.

Gtr. 2 tacet

All my life I've been search - ing for some - thing, some -

Fig. 2

Harm.   Harm.

Gtr. 2 w/Fig. 2 (x7)

Harmonic located 3/10 distance
between 3rd and 4th fret.

- thing nev - er comes, nev - er leads to no - thing. No - thing sat - is - fies but I'm

get - ting close,___ clos - er to the prize___ at the end of the rope,___

Fig. 3

are you gonna be my girl

Words & Music by Nic Cester & Cameron Muncey

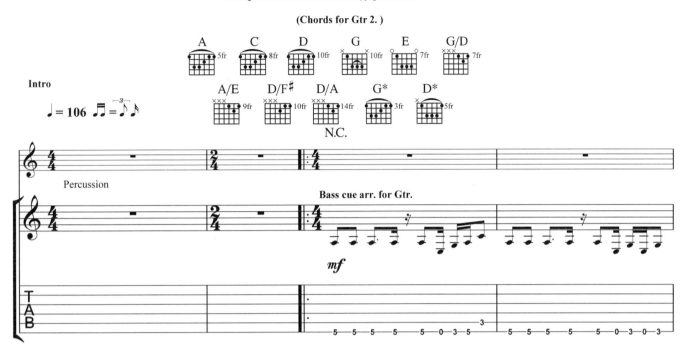

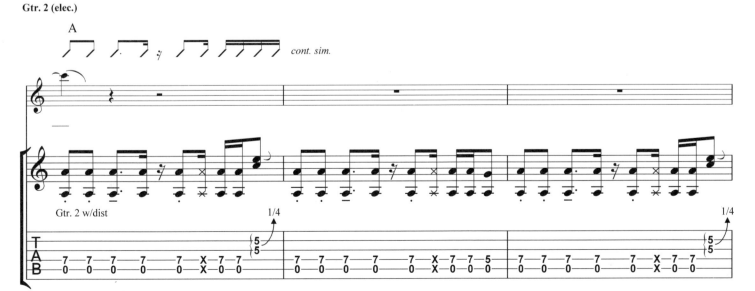

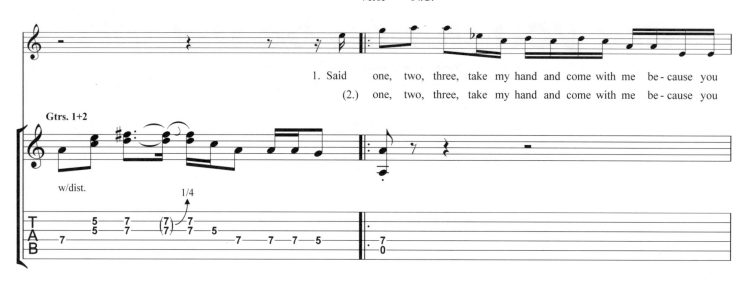

1. Said one, two, three, take my hand and come with me be-cause you
(2.) one, two, three, take my hand and come with me be-cause you

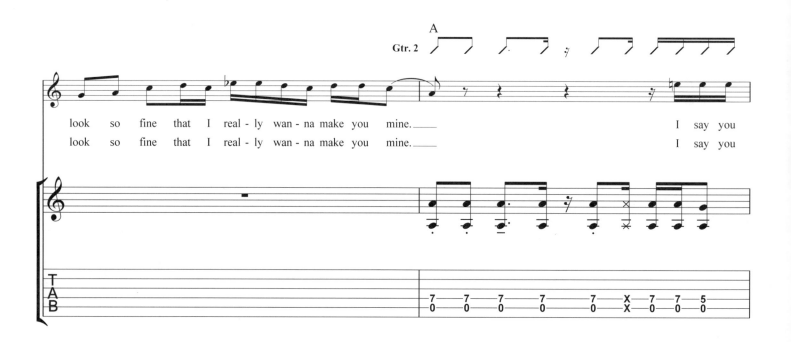

look so fine that I real-ly wan-na make you mine._____ I say you
look so fine that I real-ly wan-na make you mine._____ I say you

look so fine that I real-ly wan-na make you mine._____ Well
look so fine that I real-ly wan-na make you mine._____ Well

four, five, six, come on___ and get your kicks, now you don't need a-mon-ey when you look like that, do you hon-ey?___
four, five, six, come on___ and get your kicks, now you don't need a-mon-ey with   a   face like that, do you hon-ey?___

cont. in stave

Big___ black   boots,

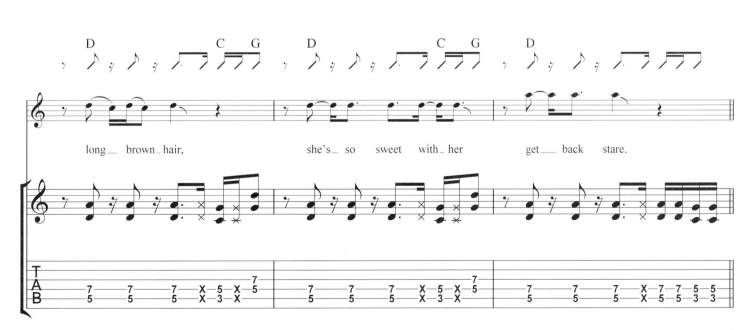

long___ brown_hair,   she's_ so   sweet with_ her   get___ back   stare.

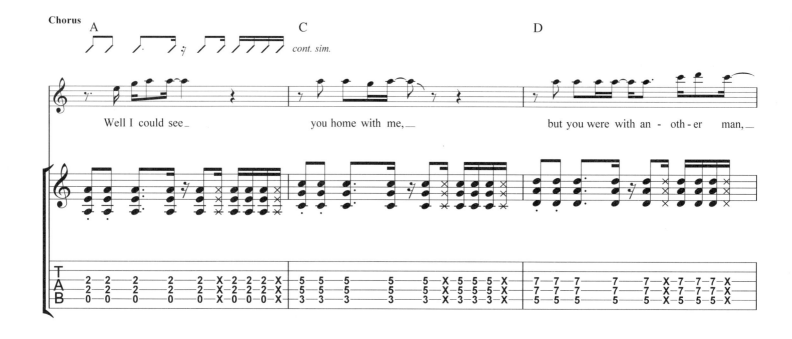

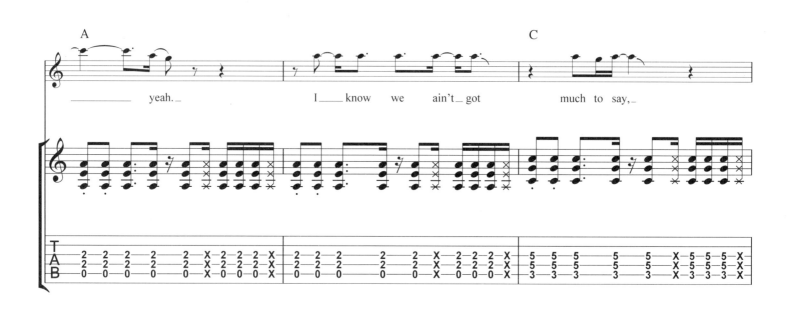

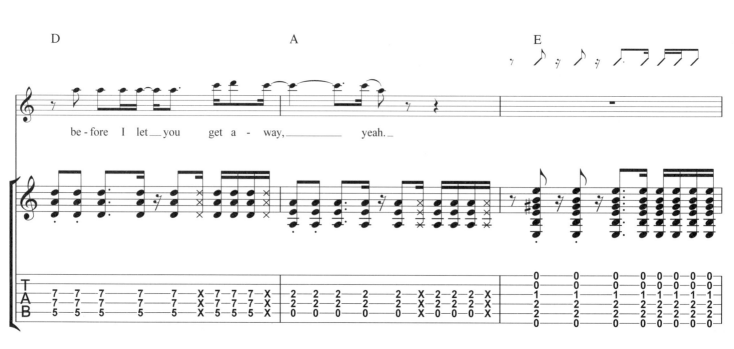

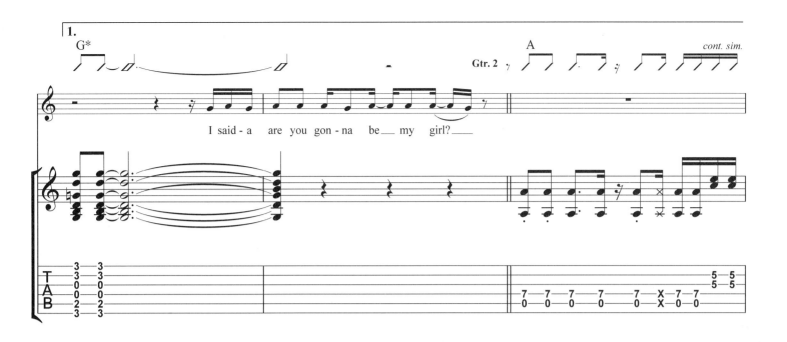

I said - a   are you gon - na   be___ my   girl?___

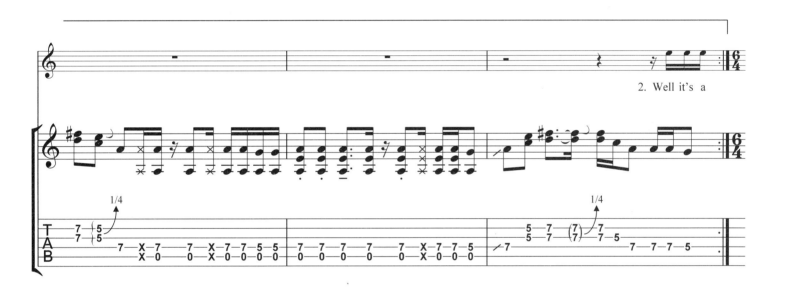

2. Well it's a

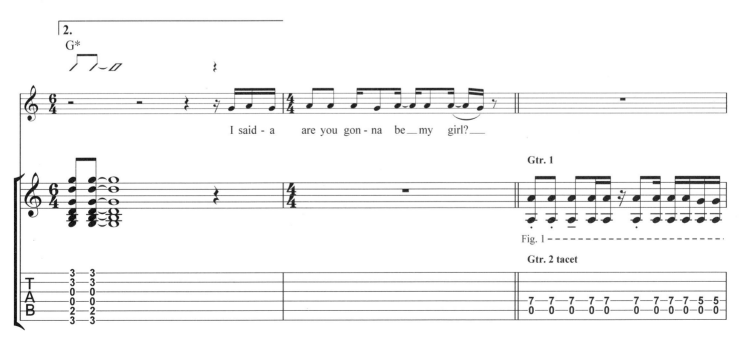

I said - a   are you gon - na   be___my   girl?___

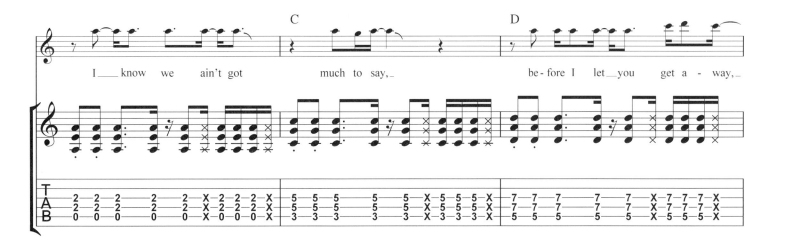

I___ know we ain't got much to say,___ be-fore I let___you get a-way,___

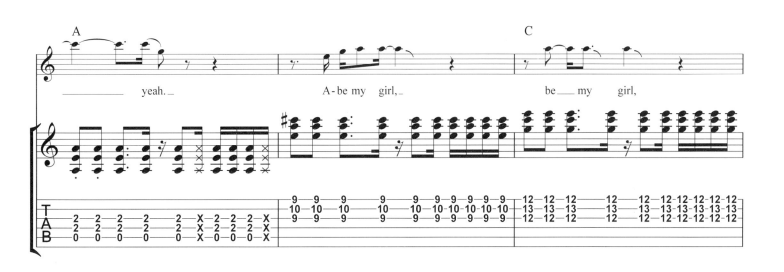

___ yeah.___ A-be my girl,___ be___ my girl,

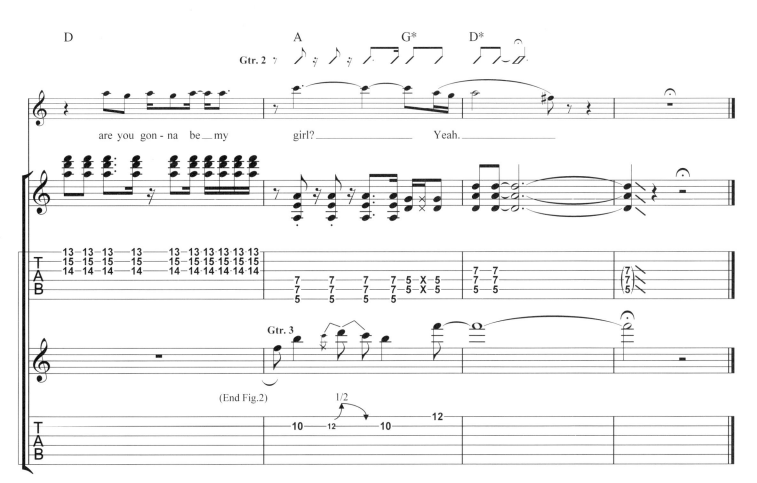

are you gon-na be___my girl?_____ Yeah._____

(End Fig.2)

bohemian like you

Words & Music by Courtney Taylor-Taylor

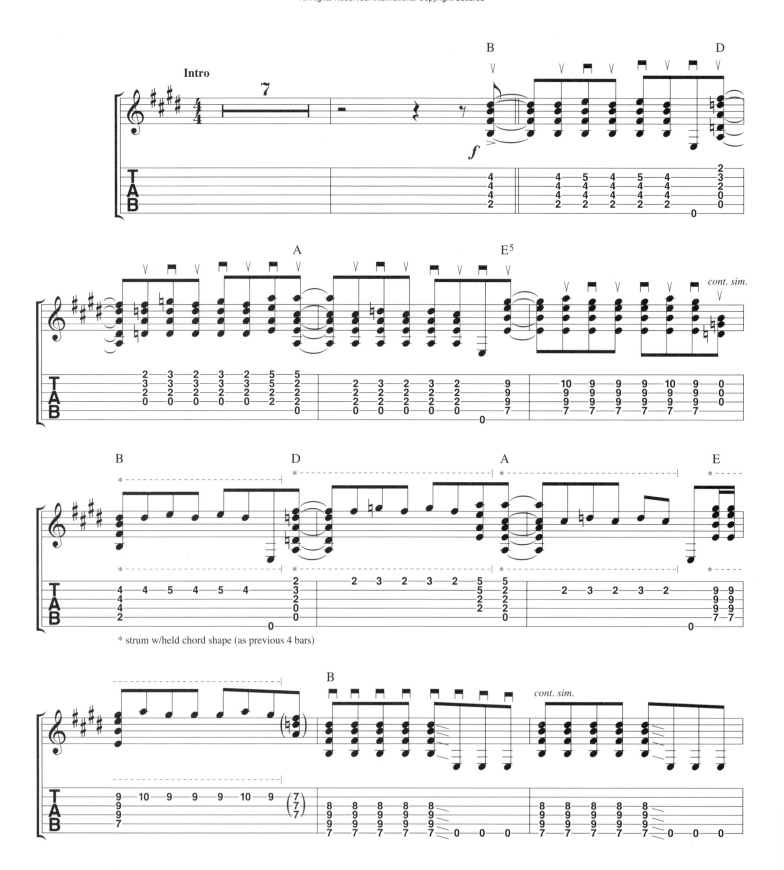

* strum w/held chord shape (as previous 4 bars)

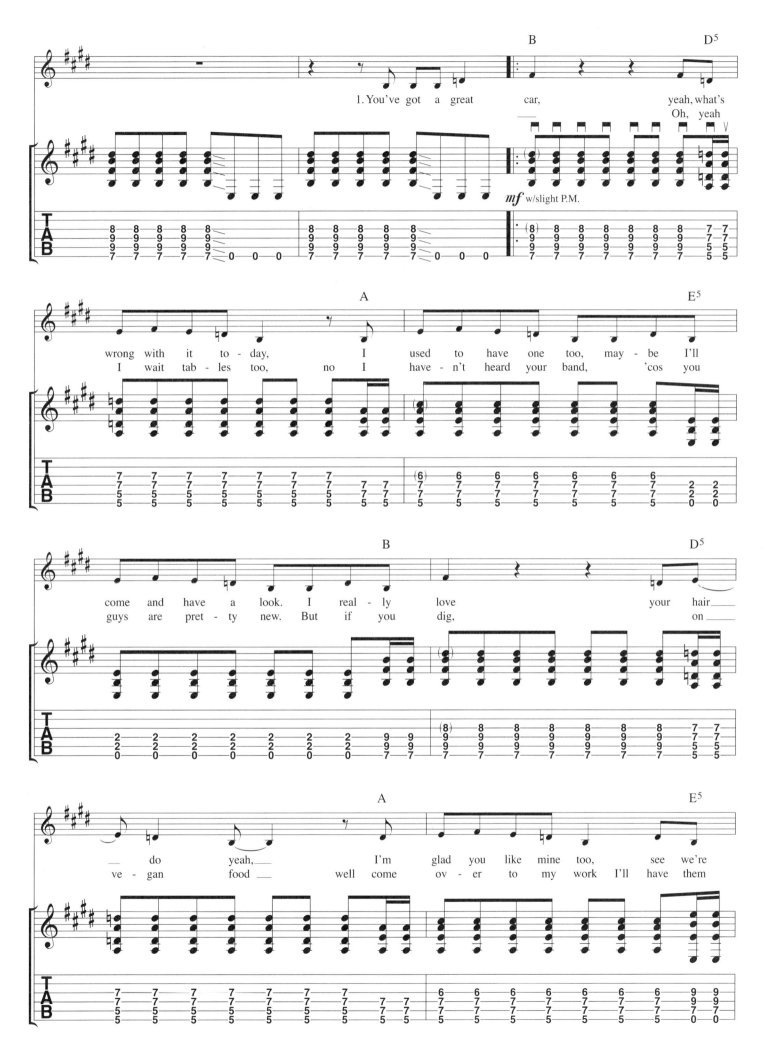

23

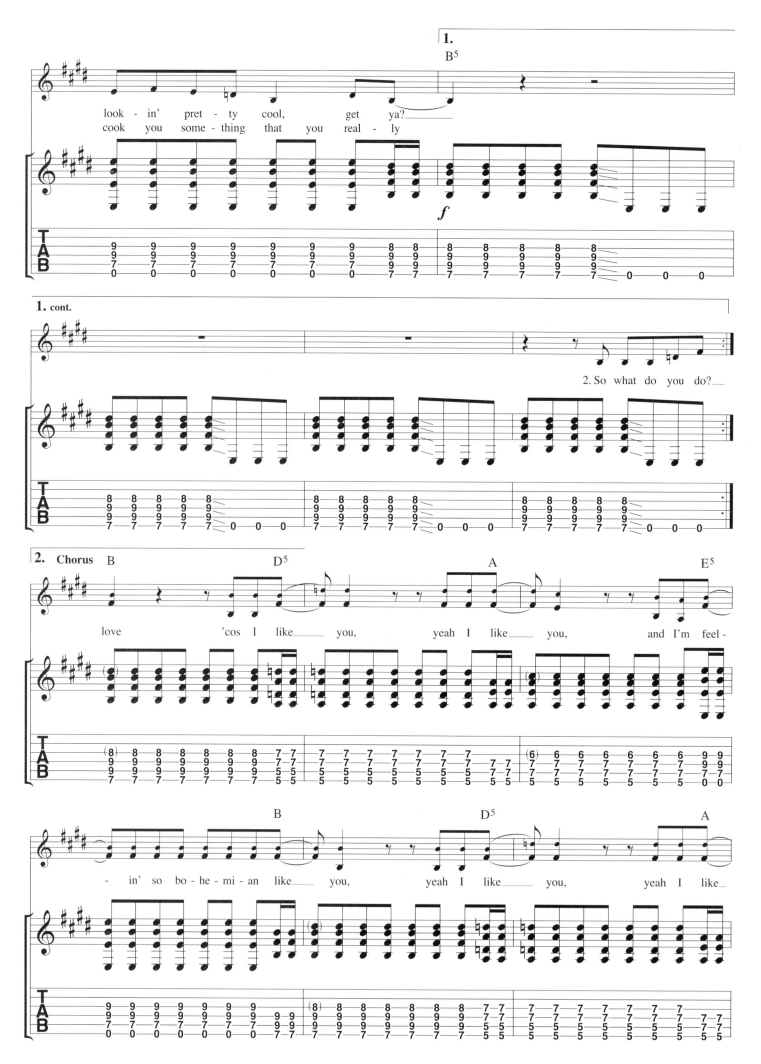

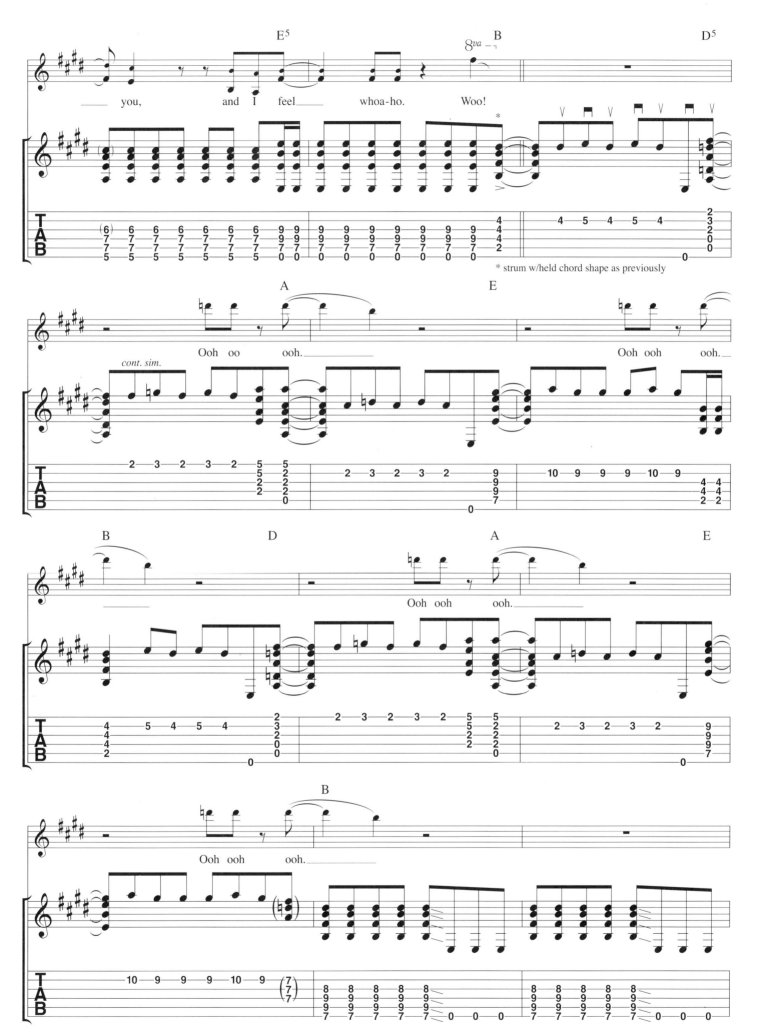

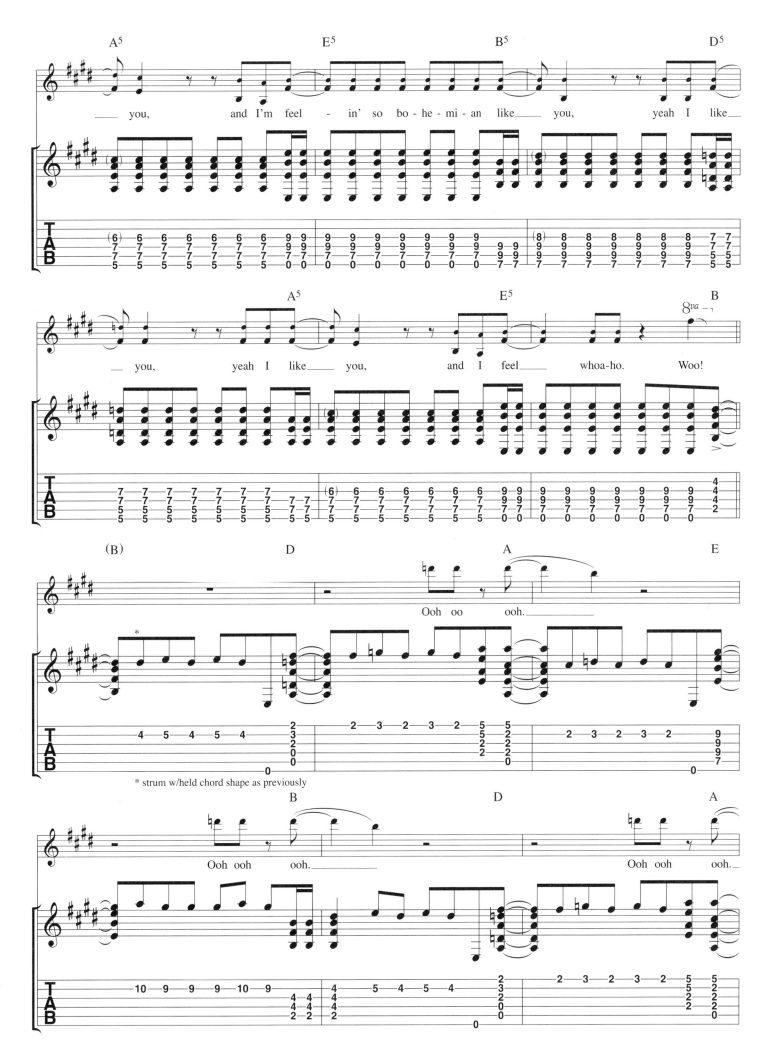

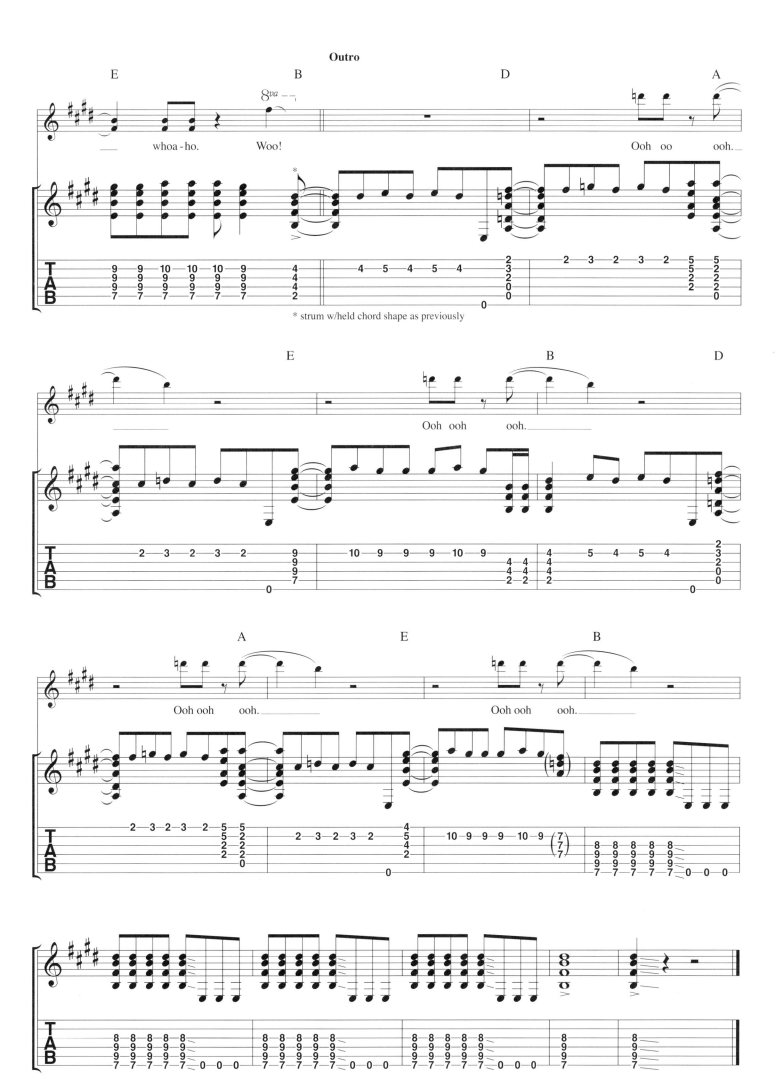

burn baby burn

Words & Music by Tim Wheeler

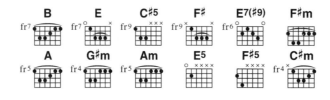

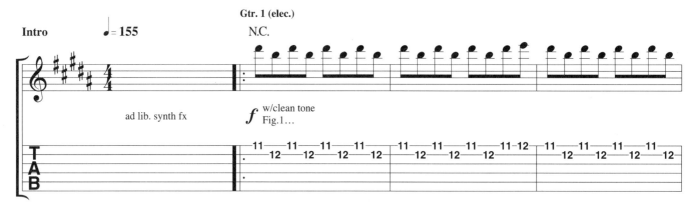

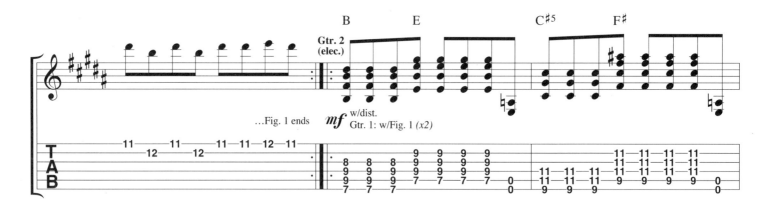

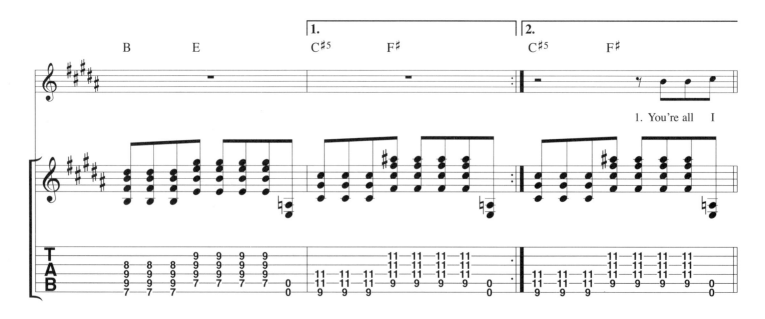

Verse

have in this teen - age twi - light,_____ your gold - en hair and your pale blue eyes,_____
2. Walk like you're in a daze,_____ un - re - spon - sive eyes in a dis - tant gaze,_____

but through all the days and the sleep - less nights,_____ we have
like _____ all the good times have flown a - way,_____ and their me - mo-

nev - er been sa - - tis - fied._____
-ry_____ leaves£ a bit - - ter taste._____

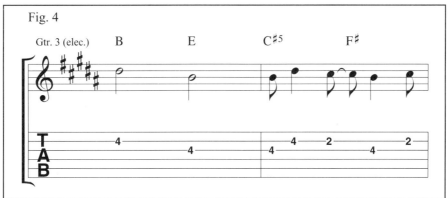

Fig. 4

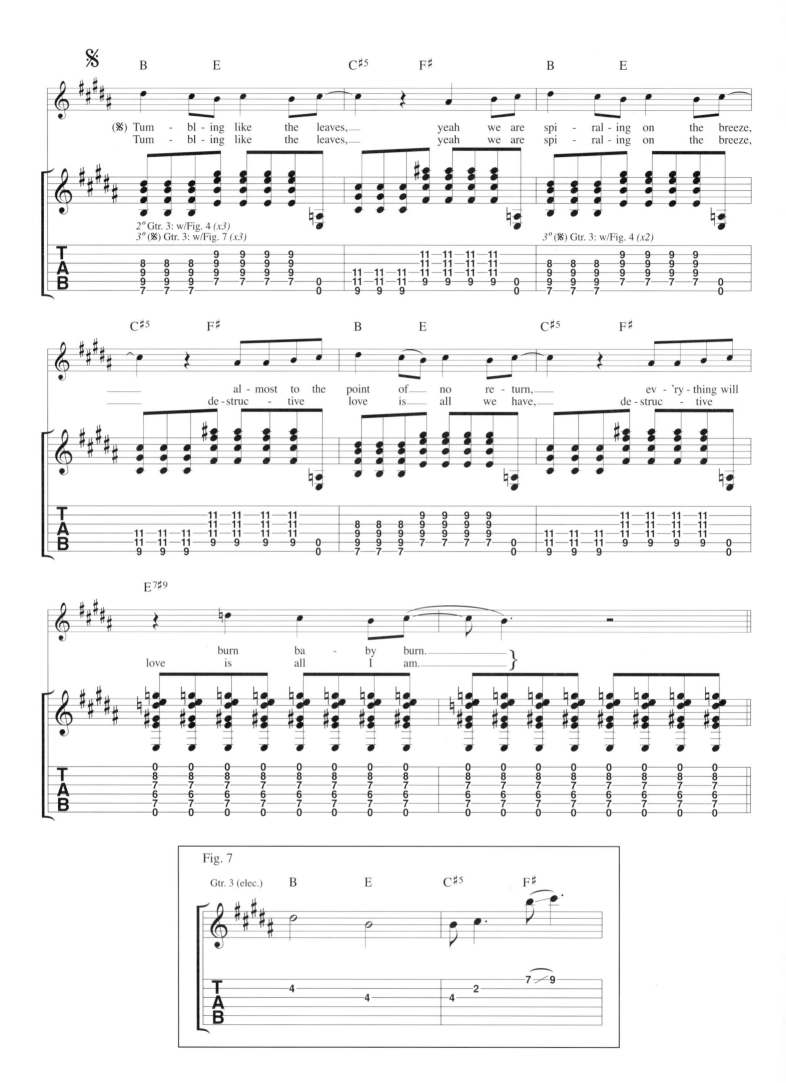

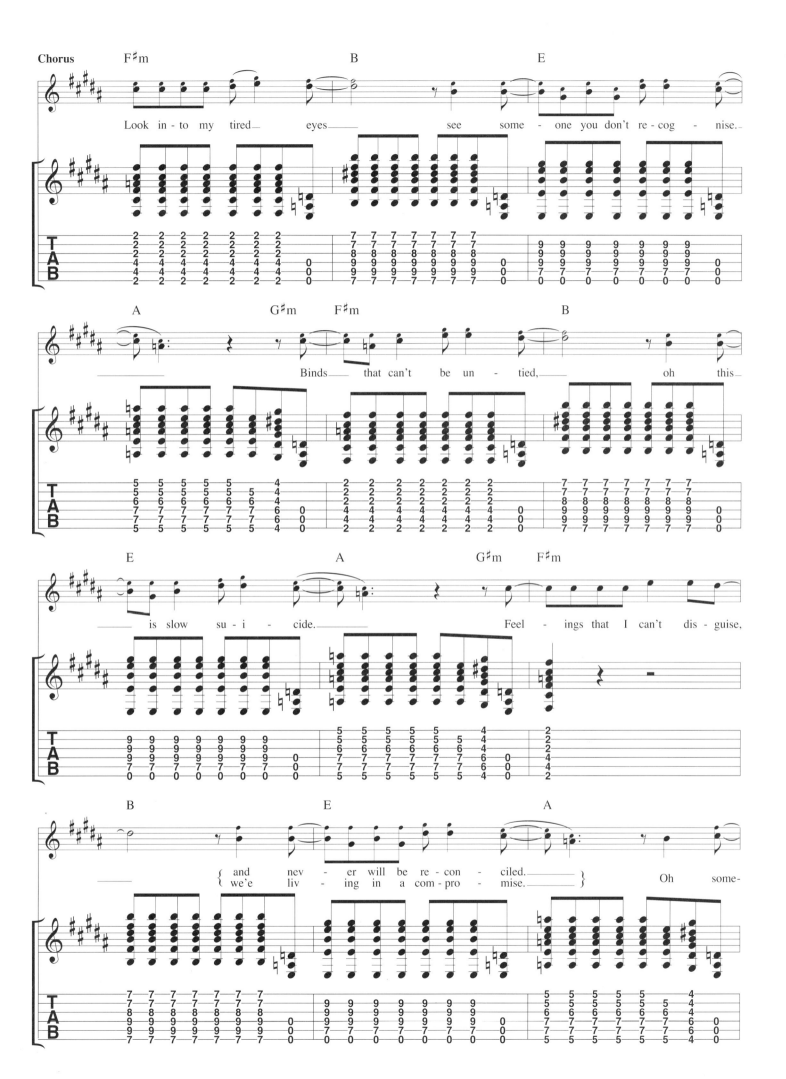

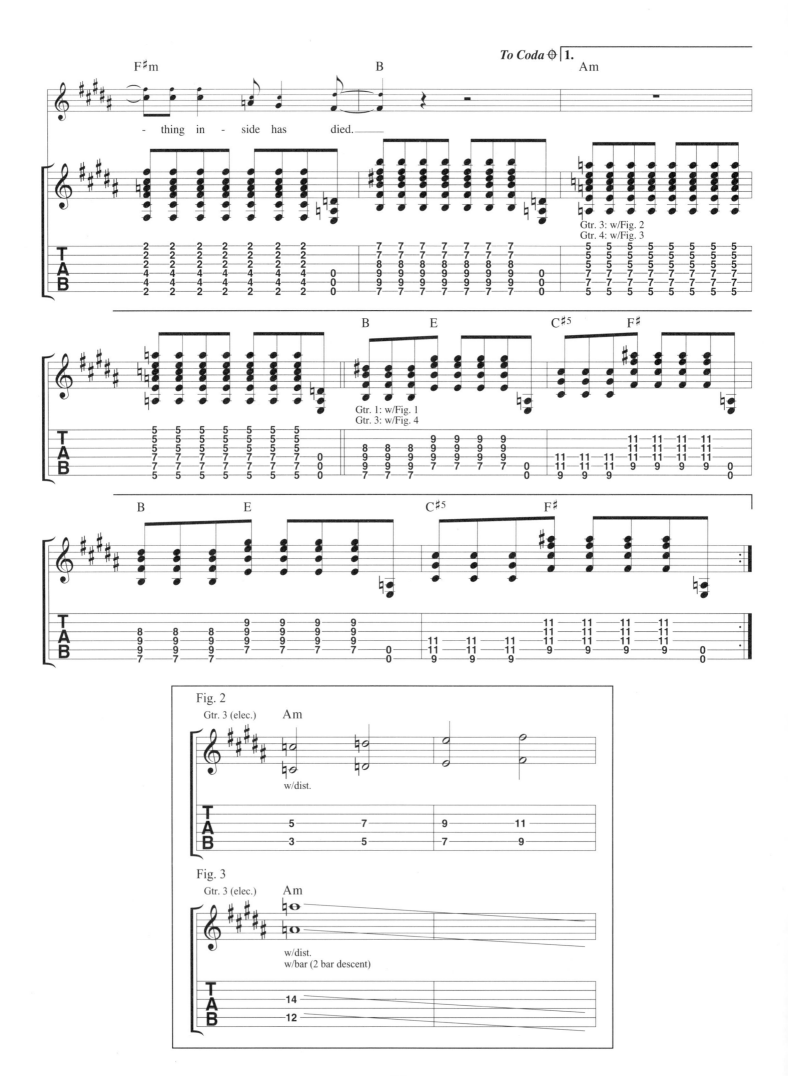

- thing in - side has died.

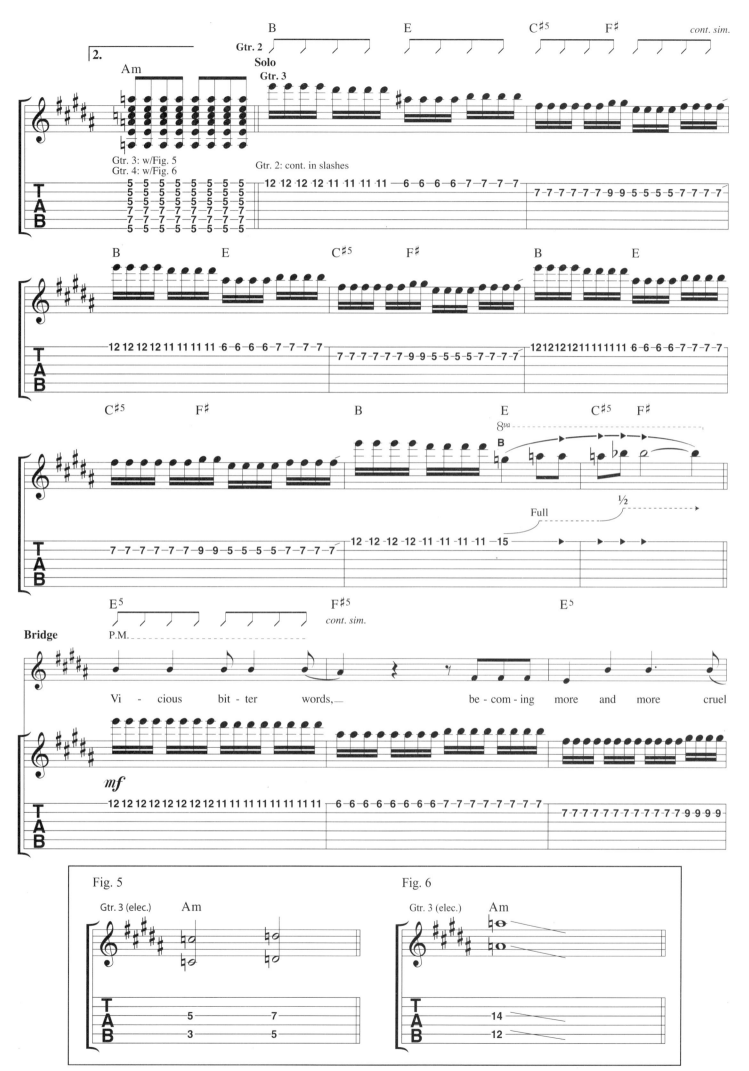

but you al - ways take them back

let me lick your wounds.

come back around

Words & Music by Grant Nicholas

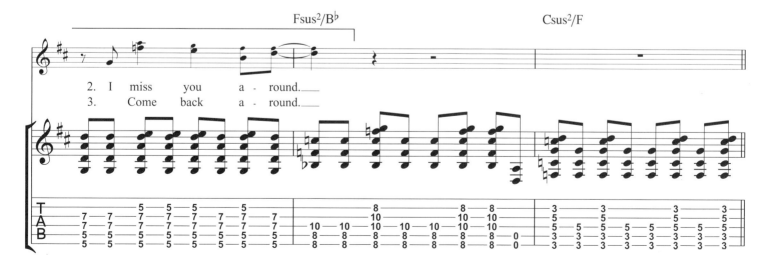

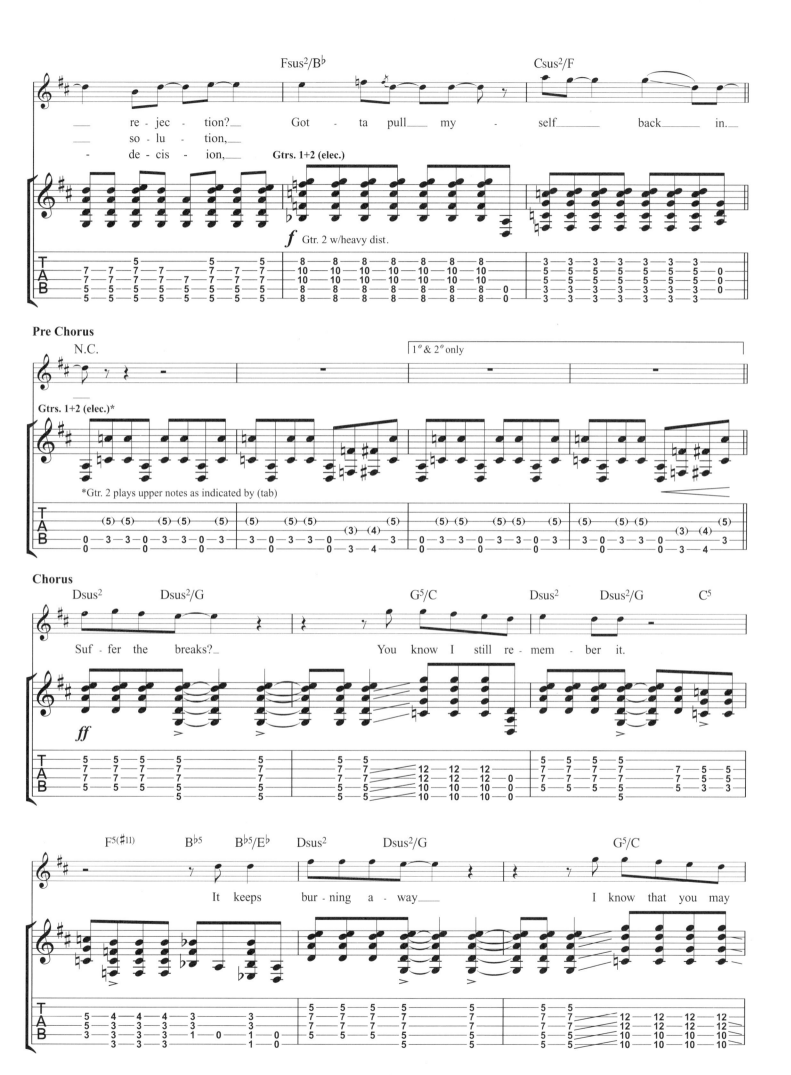

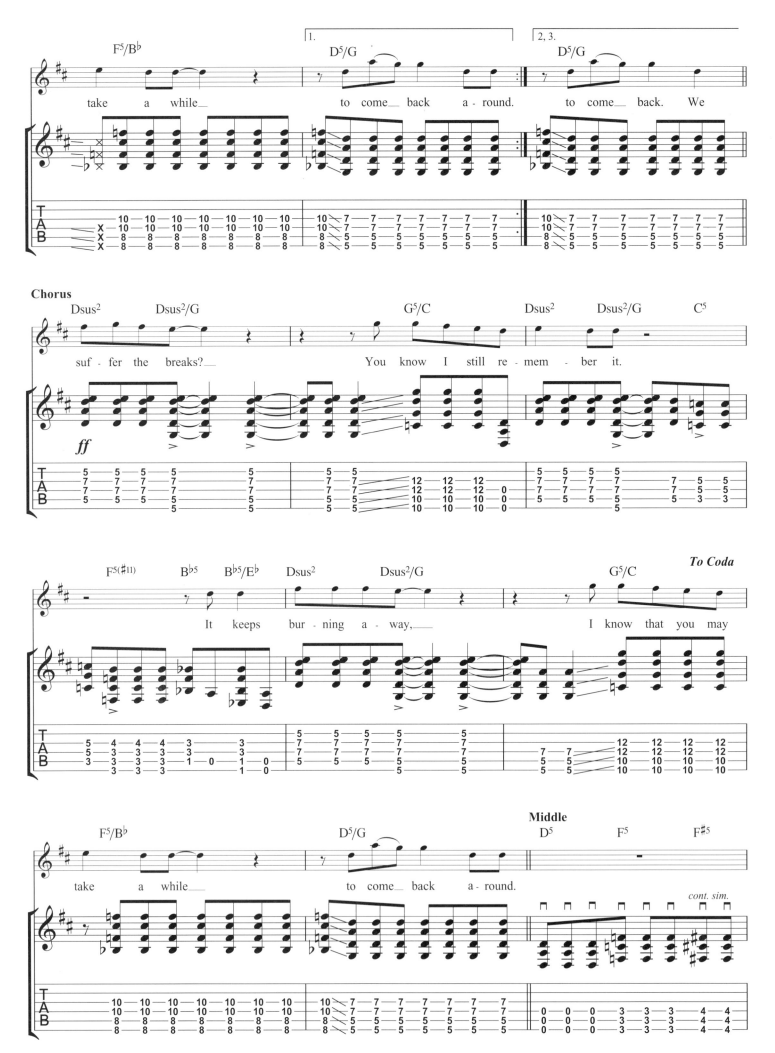

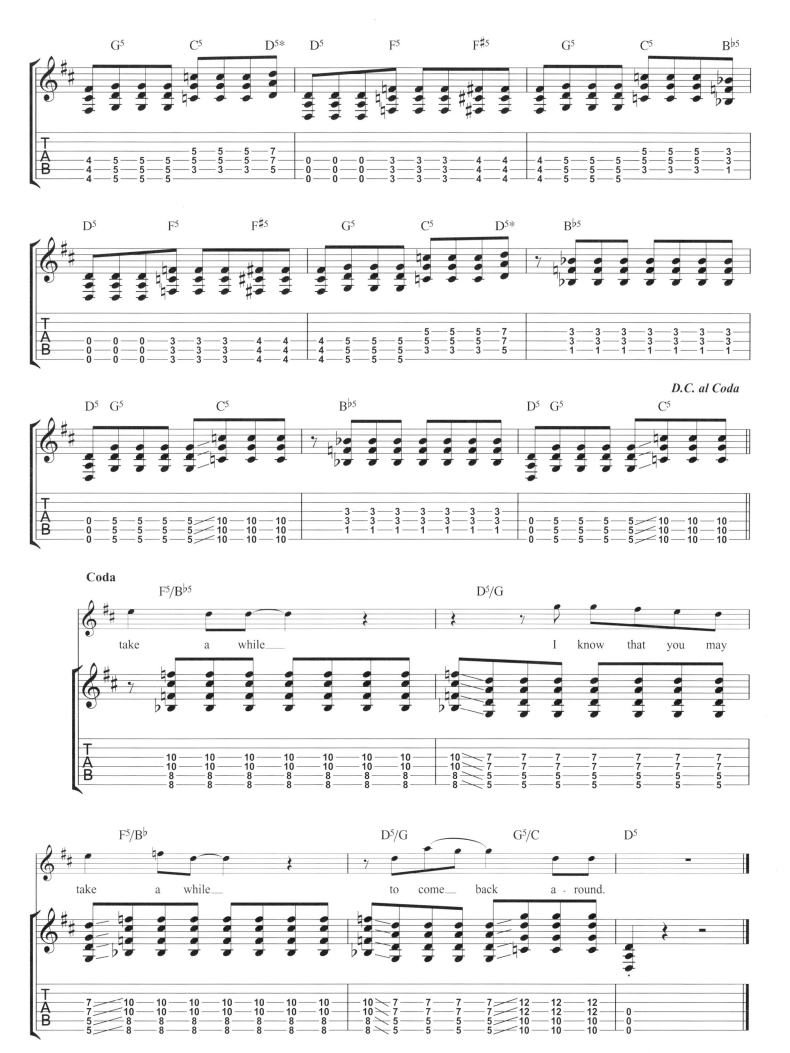

elevation

Words by Bono
Music by U2

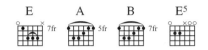

ex - ca - va - tion. I and I in the sky,____ you make me feel like I can
ex - ca - va - tion. I and I in the sky,____ you make me feel like I can

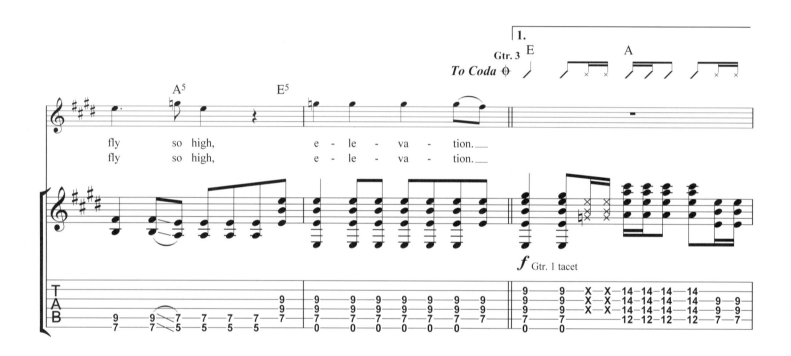

fly so high, e - le - va - tion.____
fly so high, e - le - va - tion.____

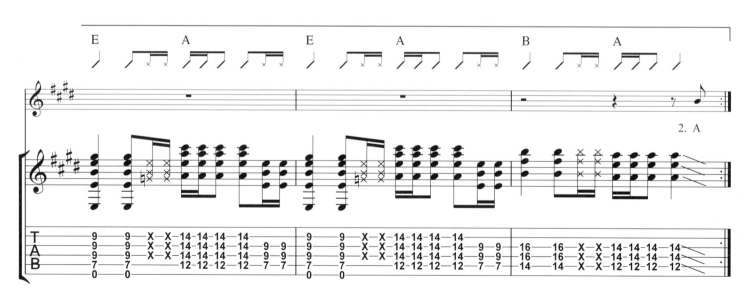

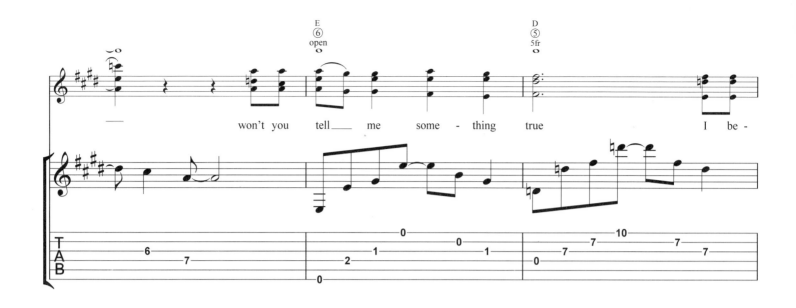

won't you tell___ me some - thing true

I be-

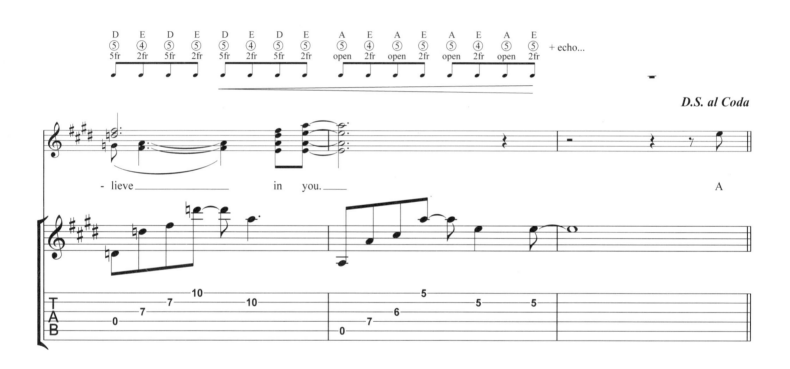

D.S. al Coda

- lieve _____ in you. ___

A

E - le -va - tion.   E - le -va - tion.

E-le-va-tion.

E-le-va-tion.

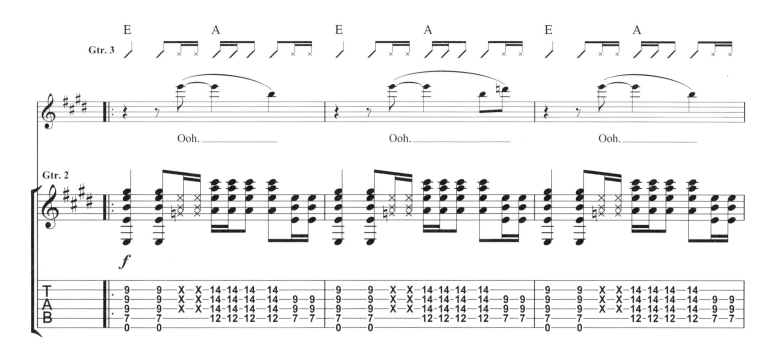

Gtr. 3

Ooh.

Ooh.

Ooh.

Gtr. 2

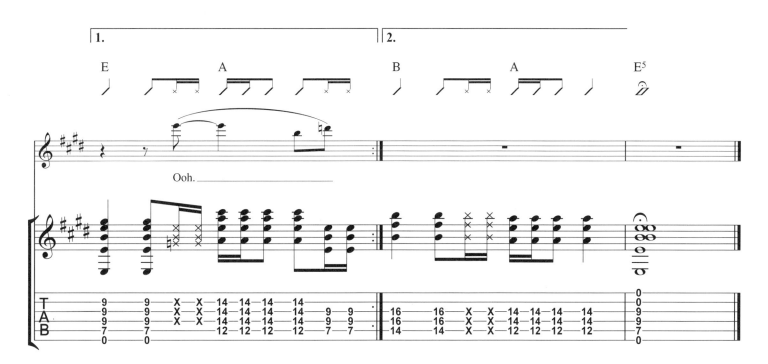

1.

2.

Ooh.

fall to pieces

Words & Music by Matt Sorum, Duff 'Rose' McKagan, Scott Weiland, David Kushner & Saul Hudson

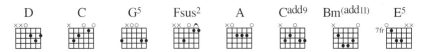

Recorded key D♭ - tune gtrs. down a semitone

Pre chorus

Ev -'ry time I'm_____ fall - ing down,_____

all a - lone I fall to piec - es._____

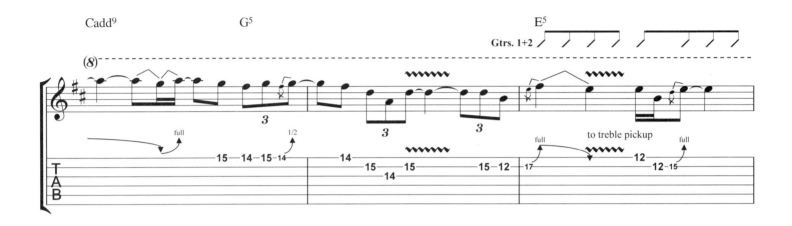

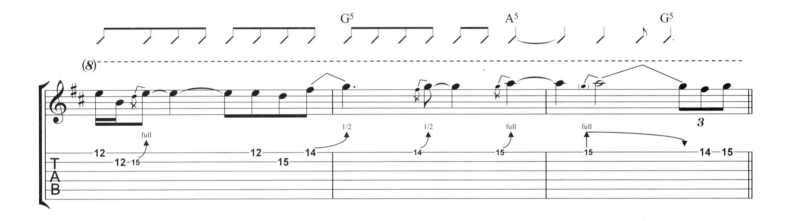

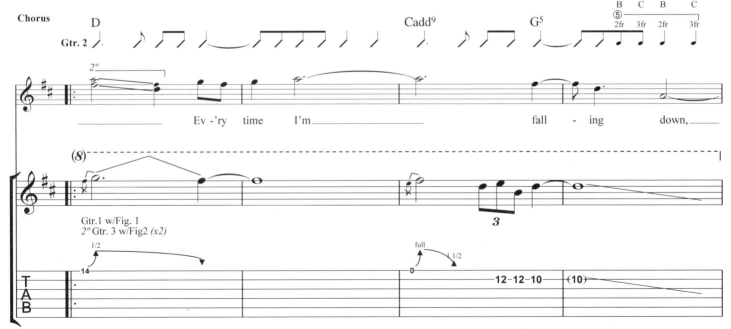

Ev -'ry time I'm   fall - ing   down,

Gtr.1 w/Fig. 1
2° Gtr. 3 w/Fig2 *(x2)*

2° play Fig.2 *(x2)* (as per chorus 1)

first date

Words & Music by Mark Hoppus, Thomas Delonge & Travis Barker

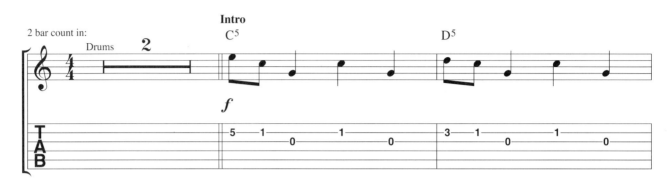

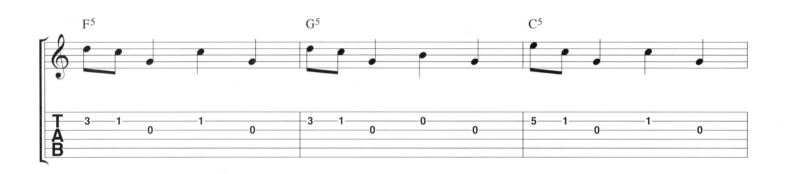

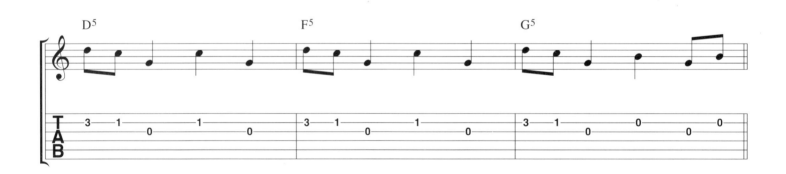

1. In the car   I   just can't   wait___   to pick you   up   on   our
2. When you smile   I   melt in - side,___   I'm   not   worthy for a

let's make this last for - ev - er.

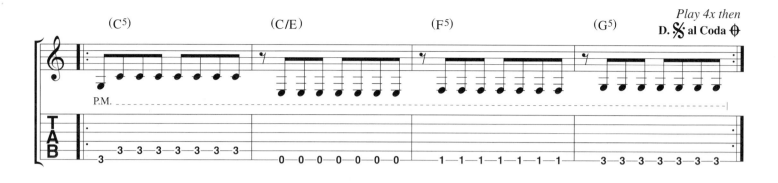

⊕ Coda

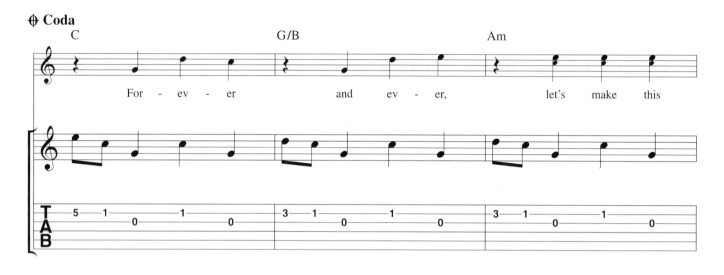

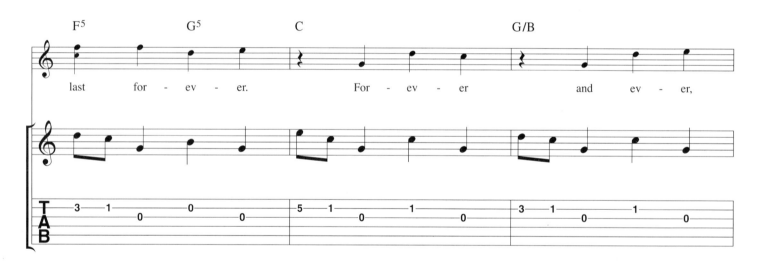

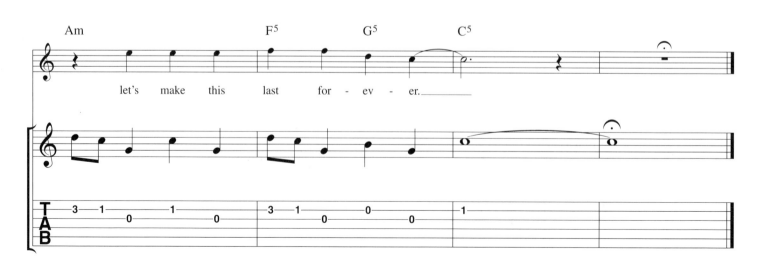

go with the flow

Words & Music by Josh Homme & Nick Oliveri

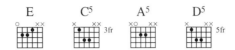

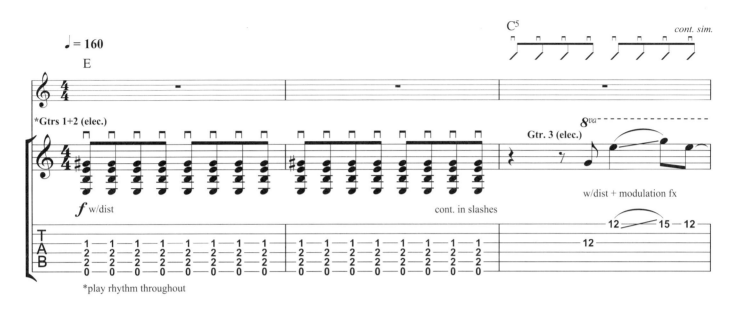

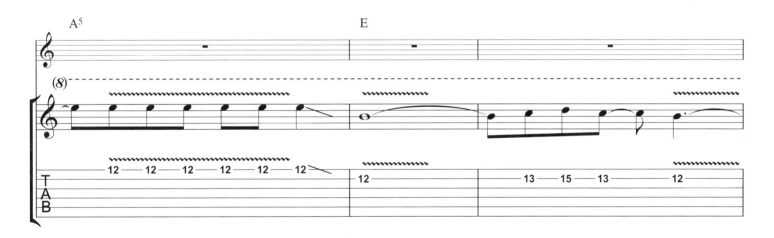

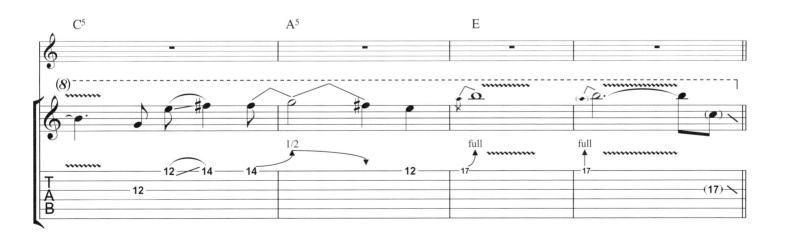

hysteria

Words & Music by Matthew Bellamy, Chris Wolstenholme & Dominic Howard

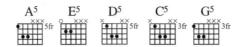

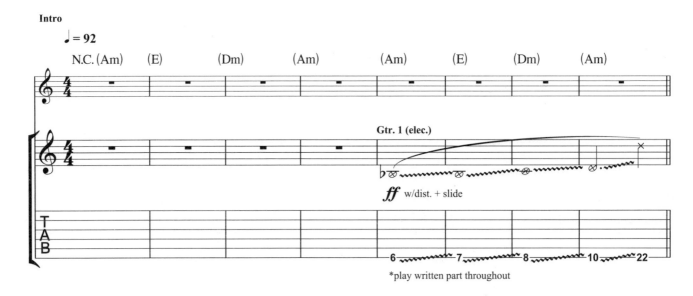

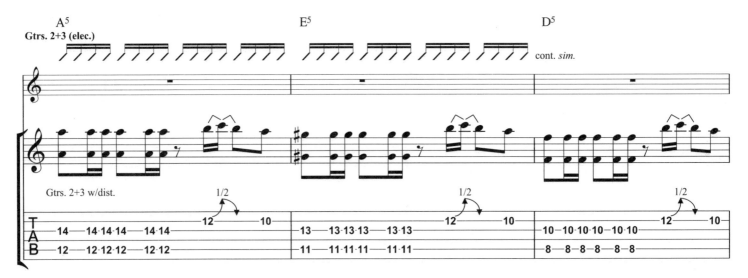

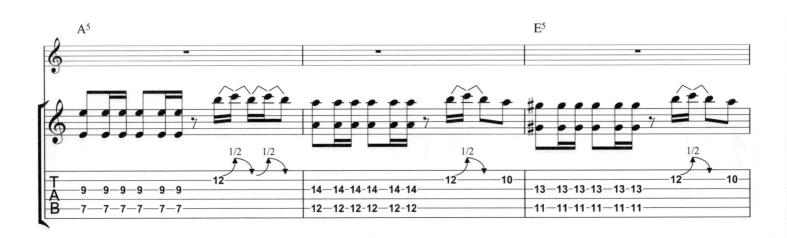

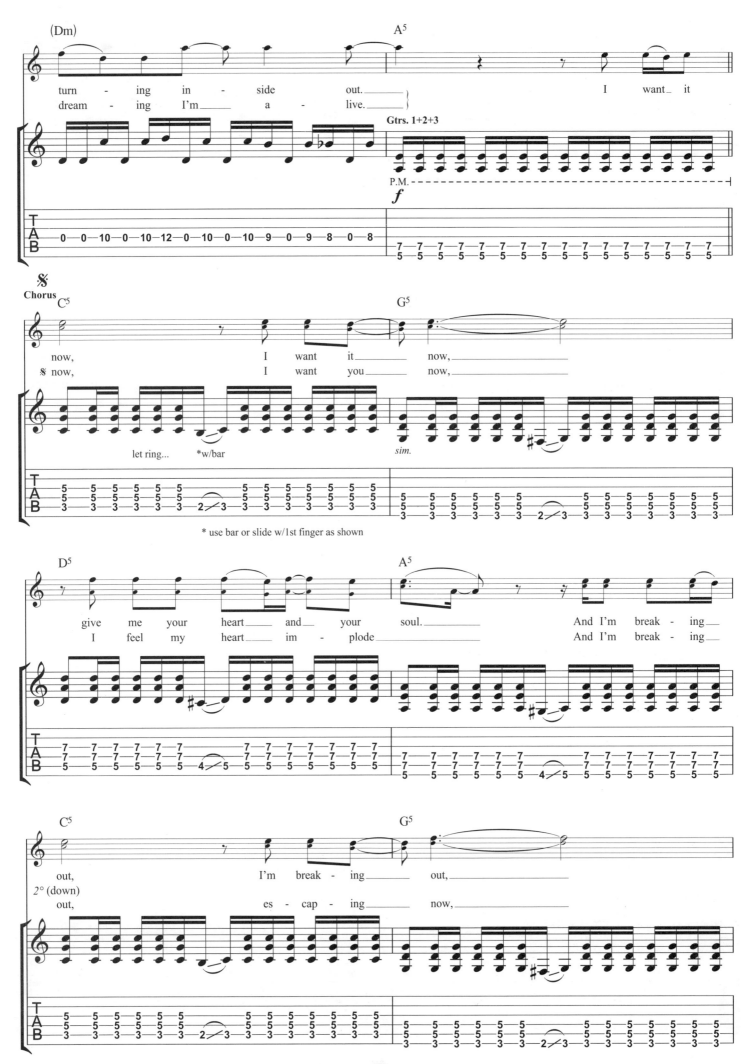

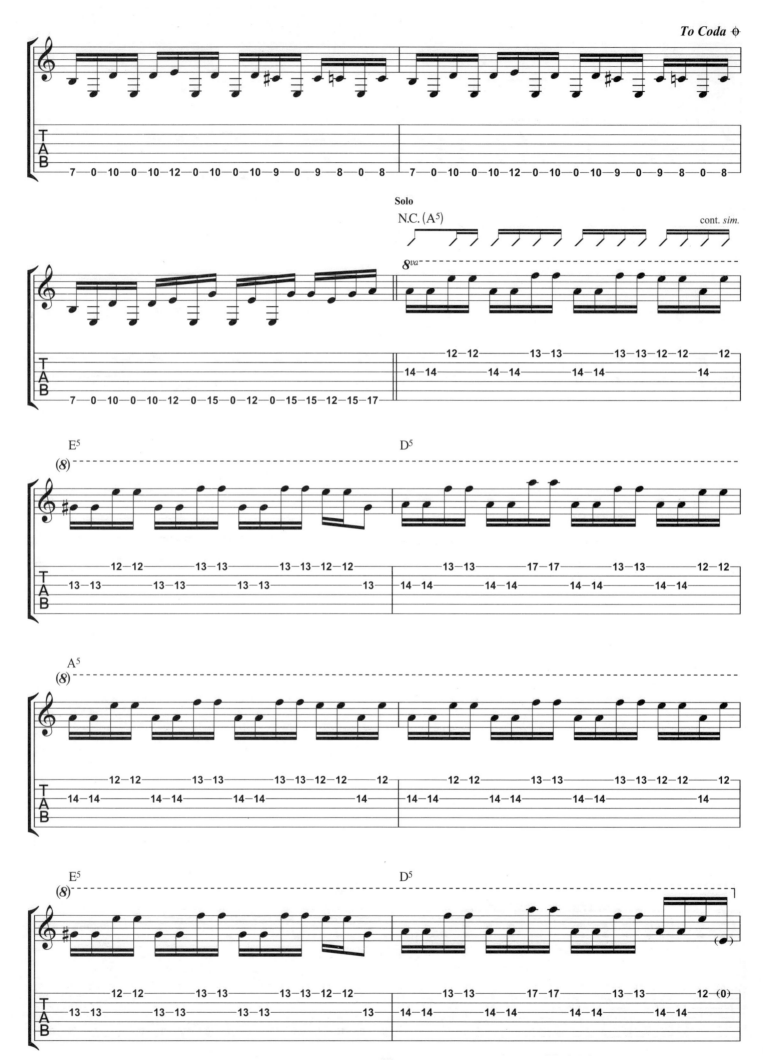

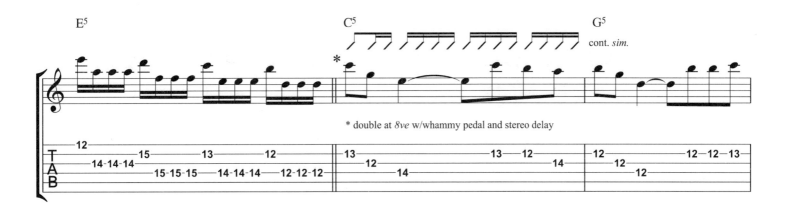

* double at *8ve* w/whammy pedal and stereo delay

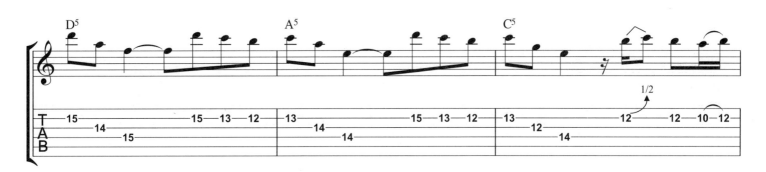

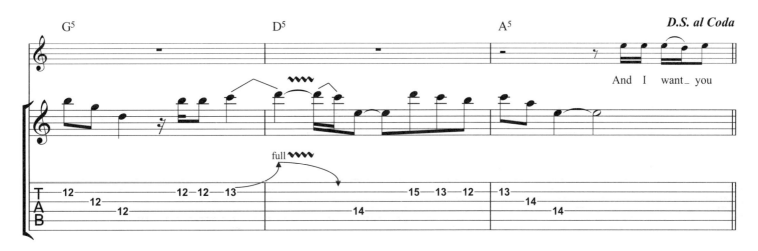

And I   want_ you

D.S. al Coda

 Coda

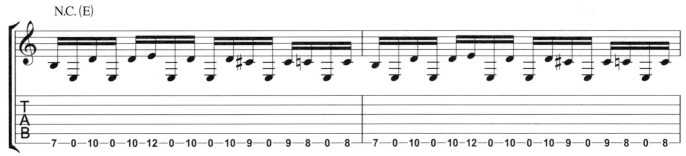

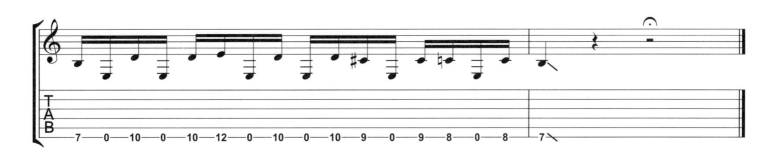

I just don't know what to do with myself

Words by Hal David
Music by Burt Bacharach

lyla

Words & Music by Noel Gallagher

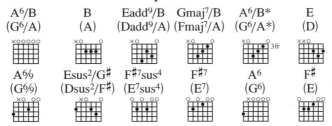

Capo second fret

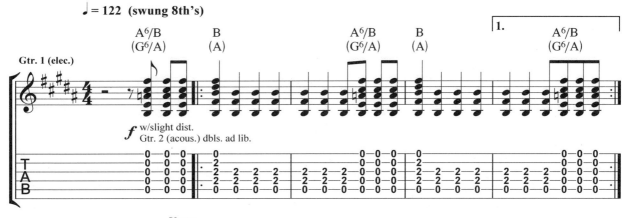

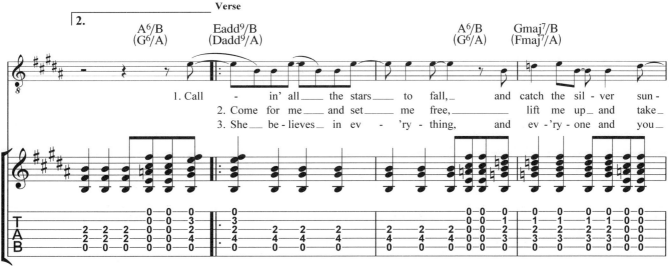

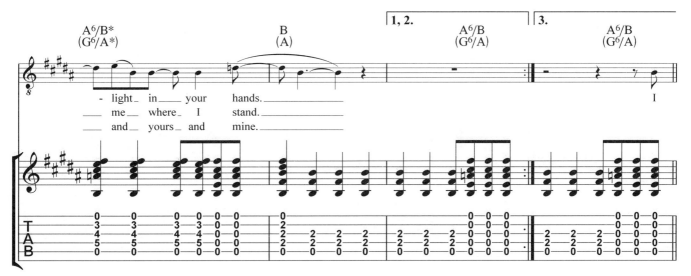

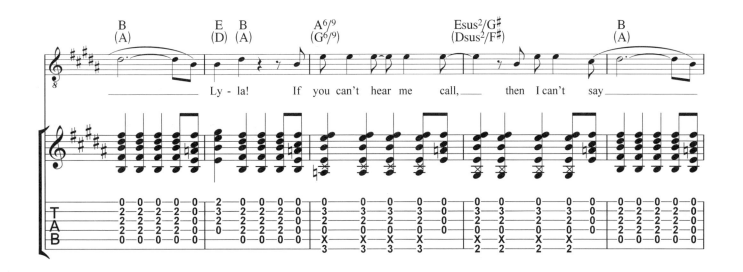

Ly - la! If you can't hear me call, then I can't say

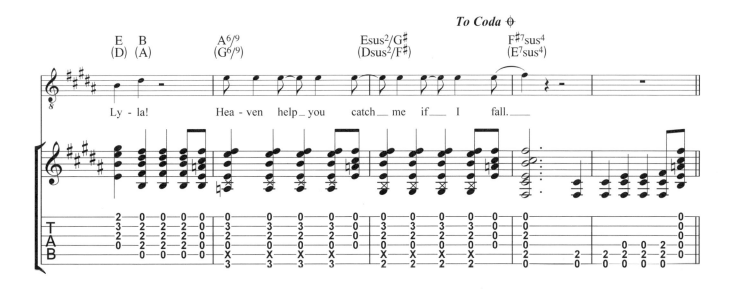

Ly - la! Hea - ven help you catch me if I fall.

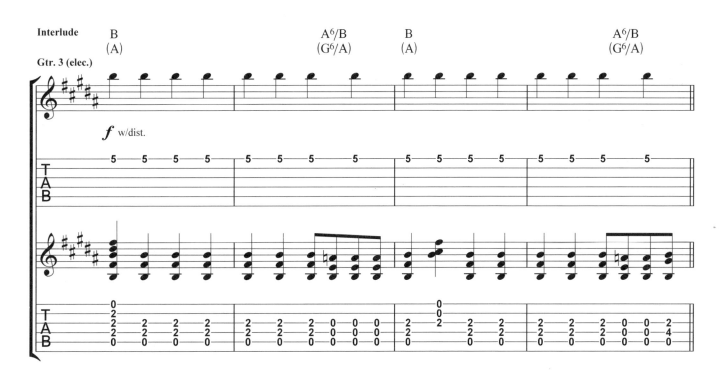

80

just because

Words & Music by Perry Farrell, Dave Navarro, Chris Chaney, Stephen Perkins & Bob Ezrin

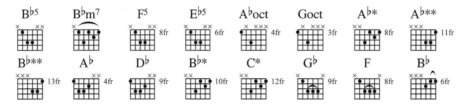

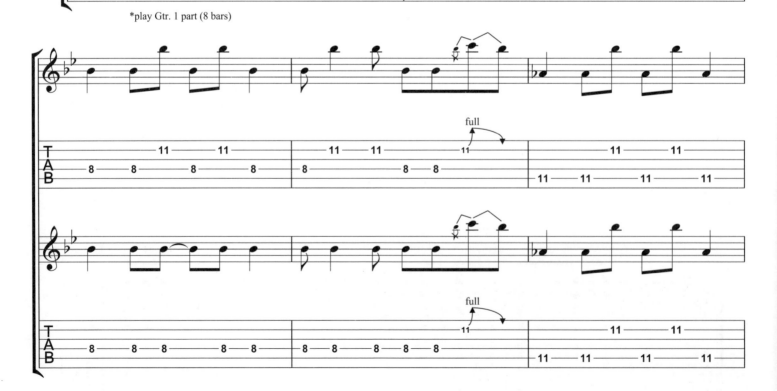

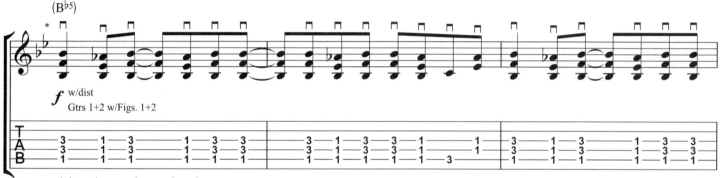

*play written part in stave throughout

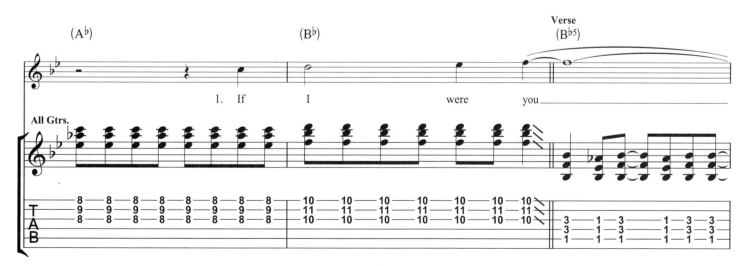

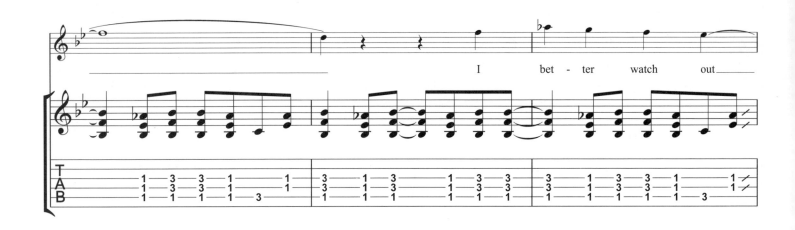

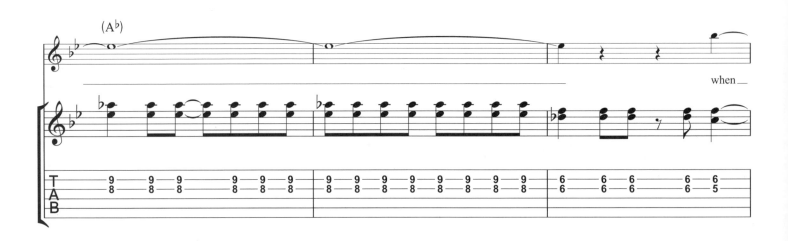

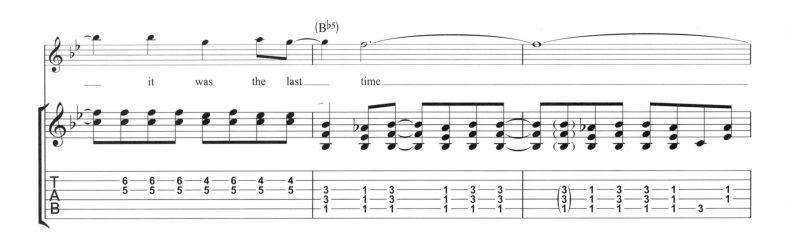

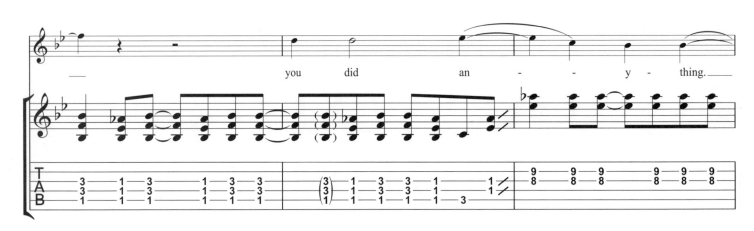

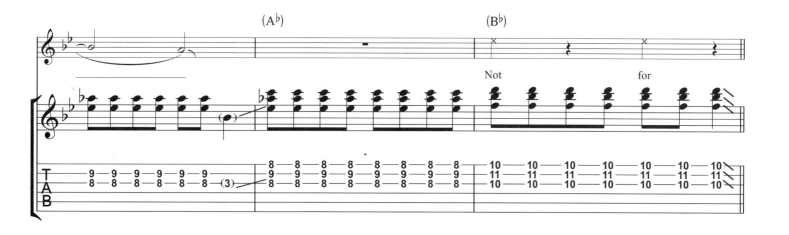

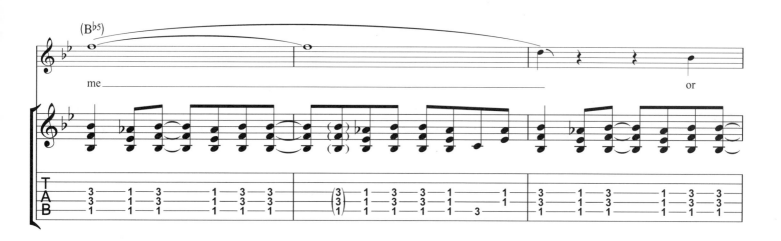

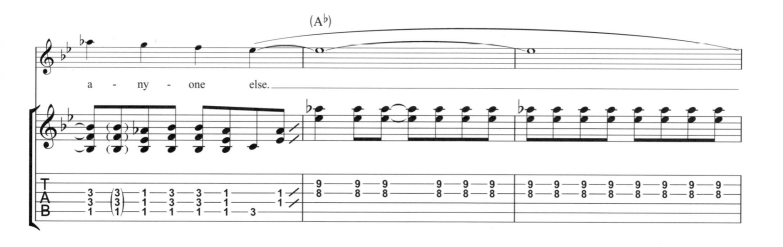

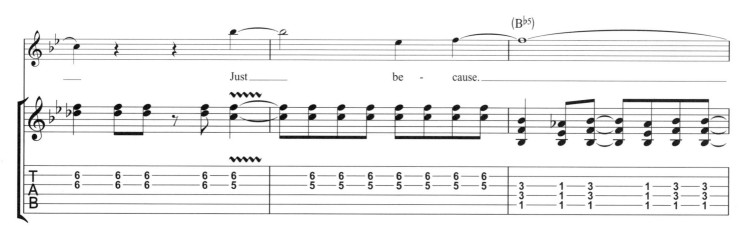

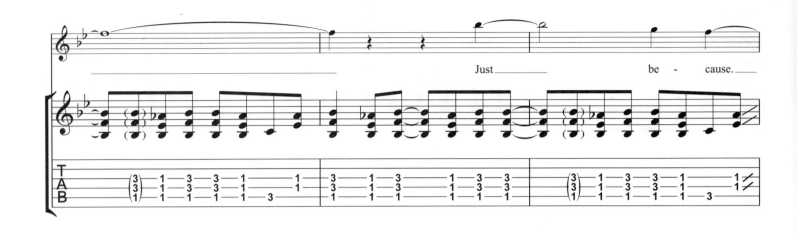

Just_____ be - cause._____

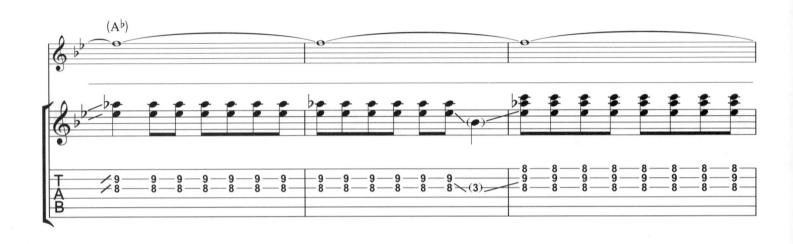

(A♭)

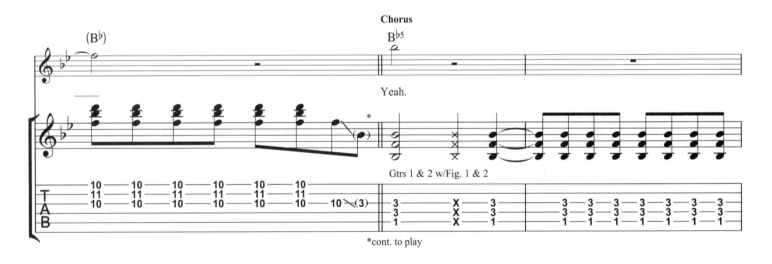

(B♭)

Chorus

B♭5

Yeah.

Gtrs 1 & 2 w/Fig. 1 & 2

*cont. to play

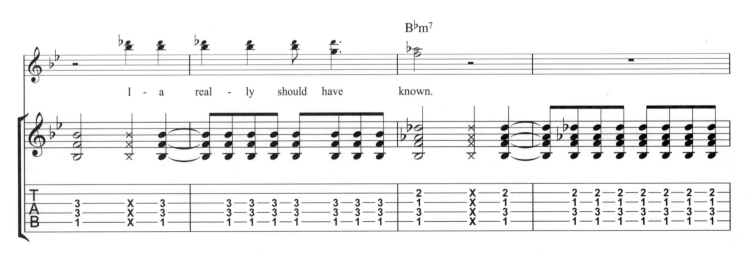

B♭m⁷

I - a real - ly should have known.

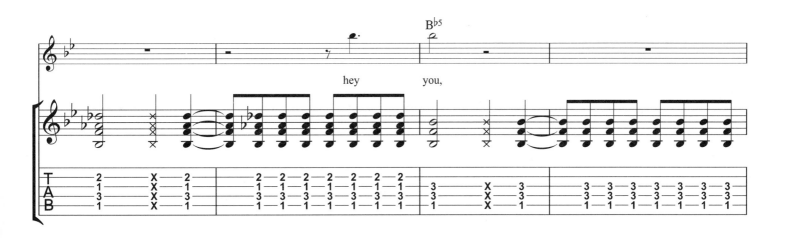

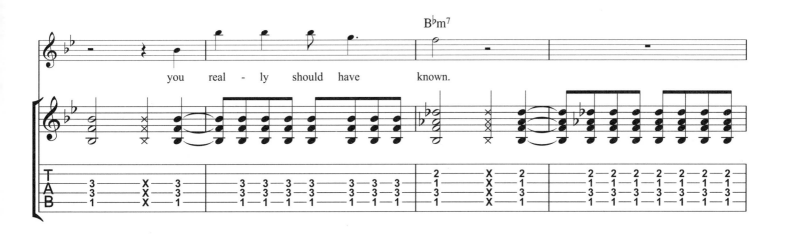

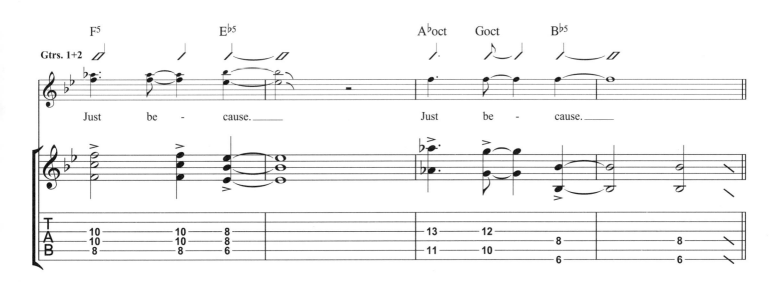

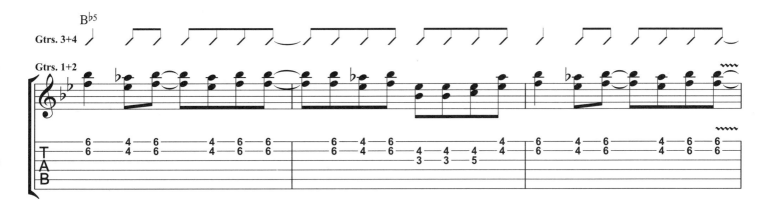

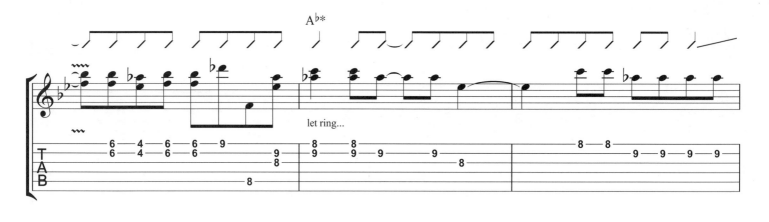

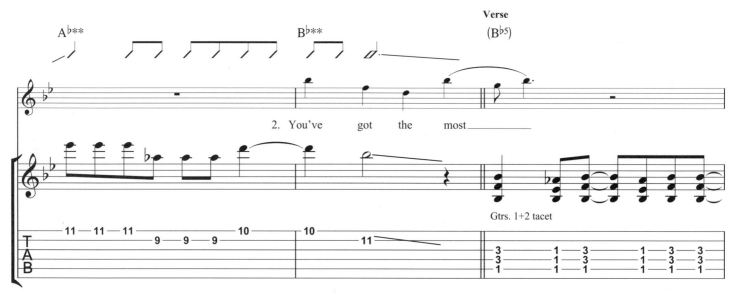

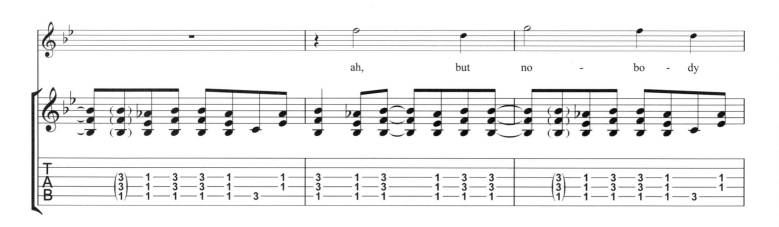

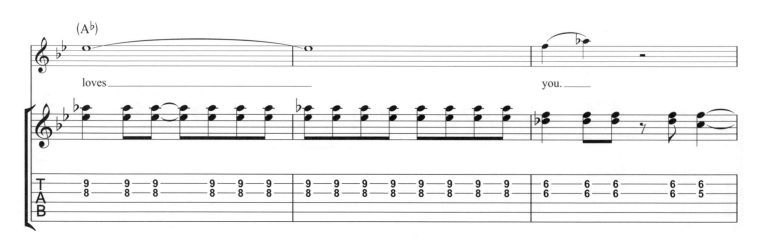

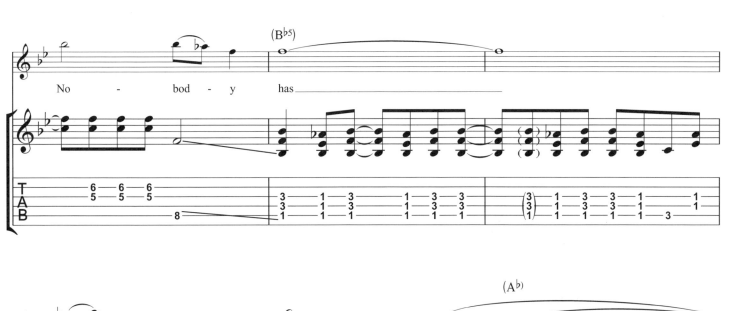

No - bod - y has ____ (B♭5)

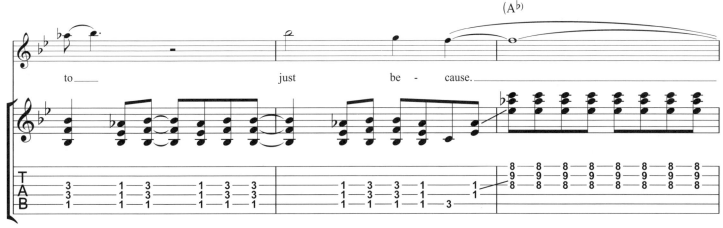

to ____ just be - cause. ____ (A♭)

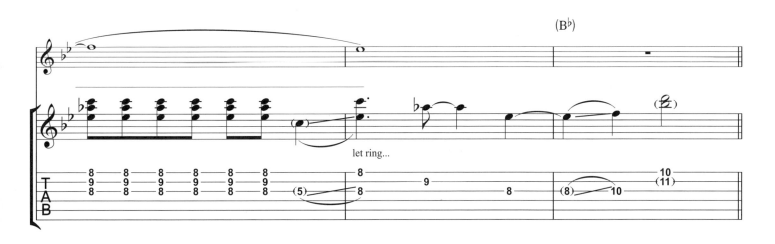

(B♭)

let ring...

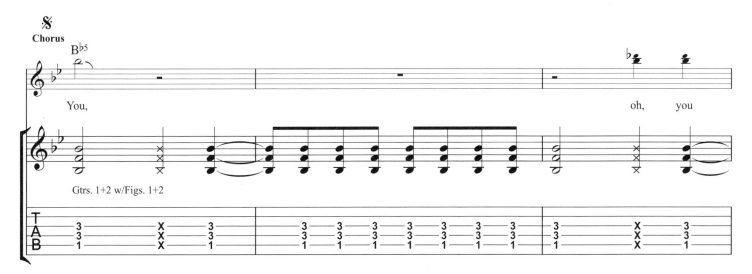

Chorus
B♭5

You, ____ oh, you

Gtrs. 1+2 w/Figs. 1+2

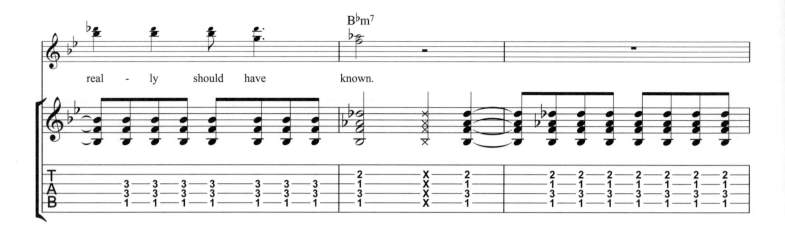

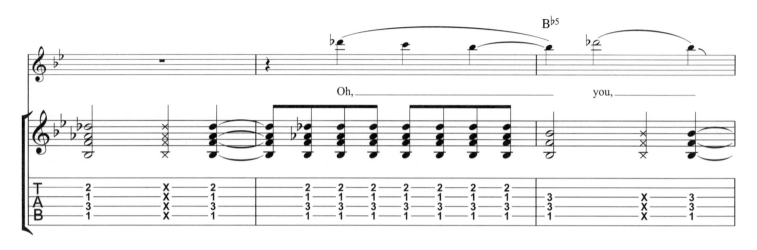

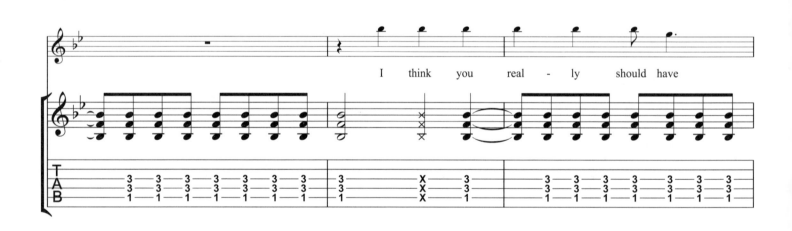

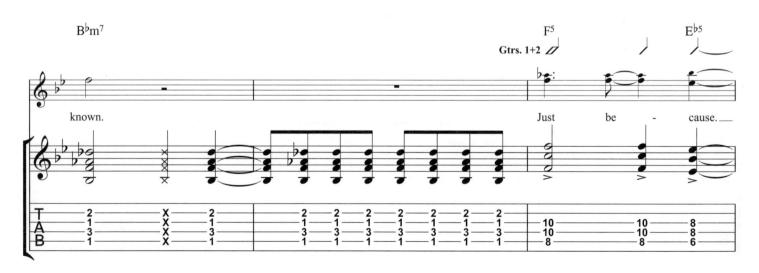

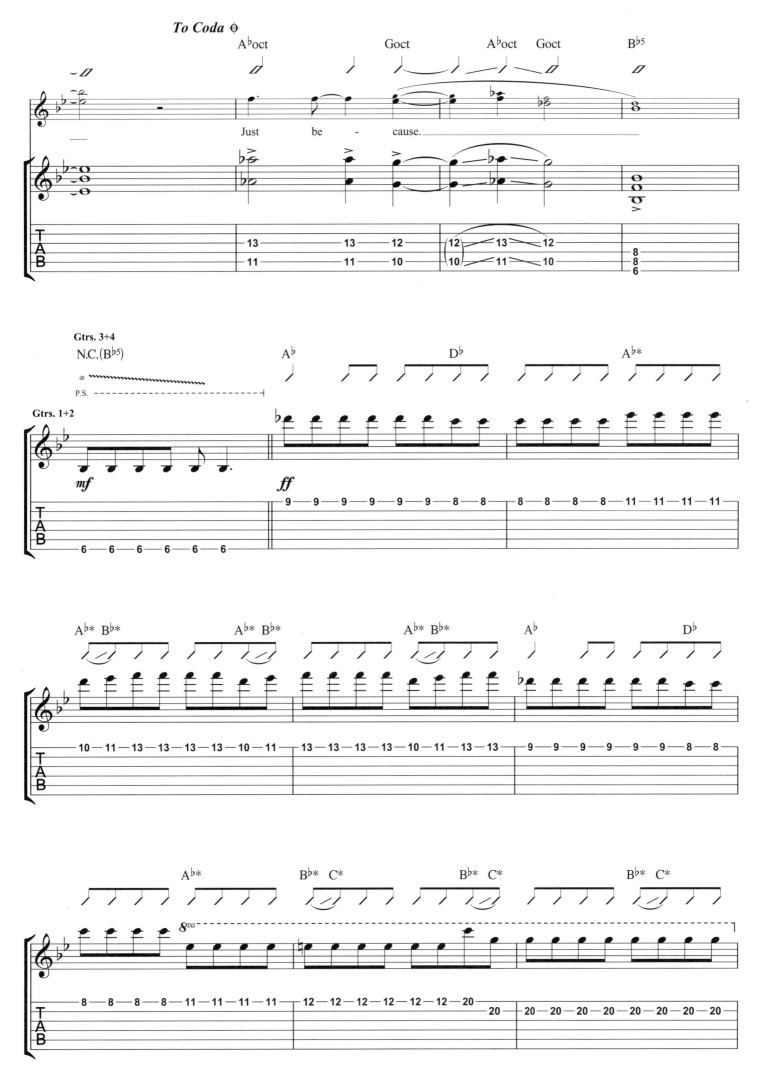

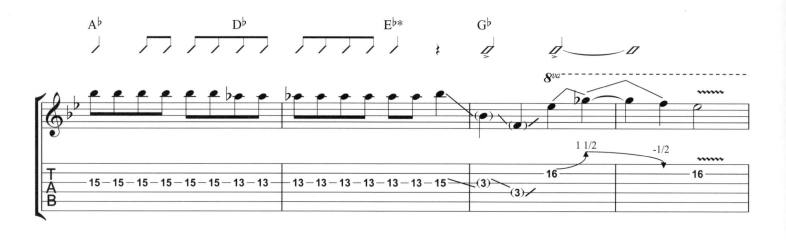

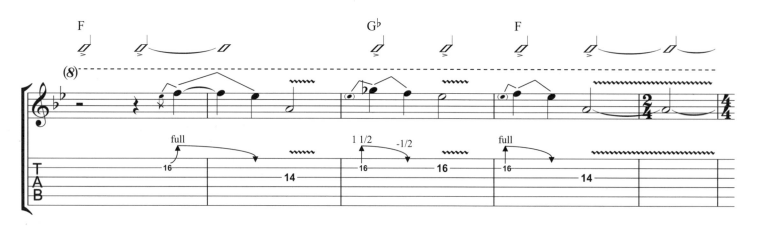

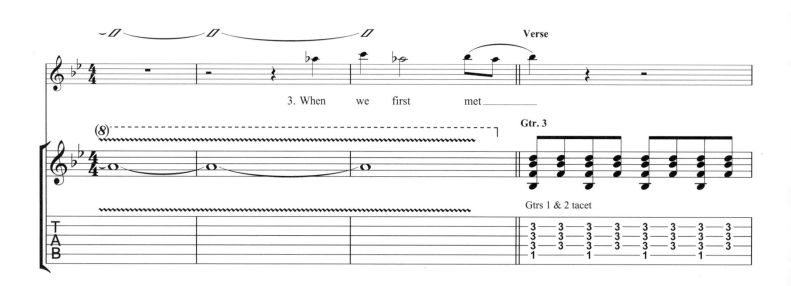

3. When we first met _____

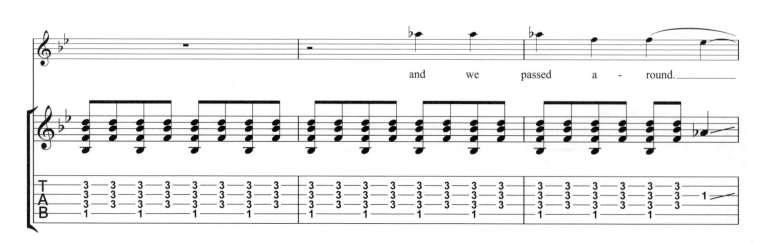

and we passed a - round. _____

92

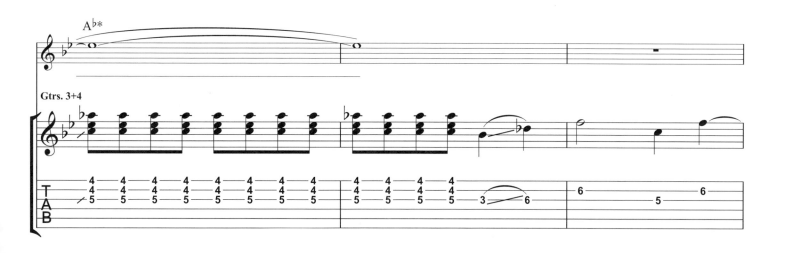

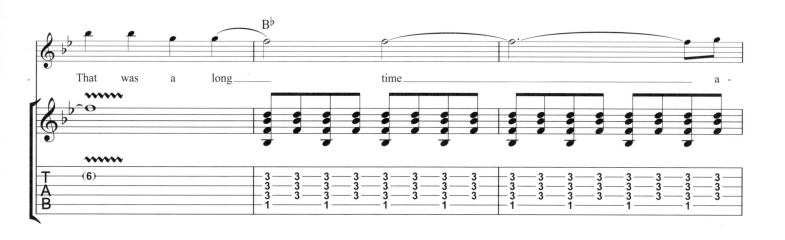

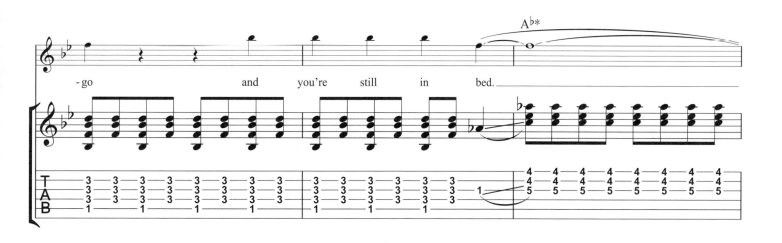

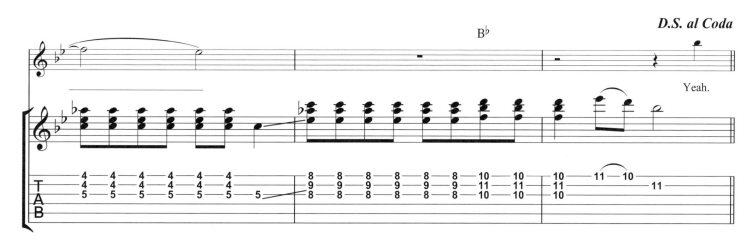

Just be - cause.

Just be - cause.

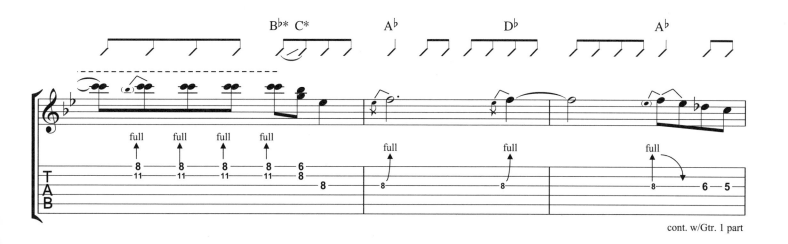

cont. w/Gtr. 1 part

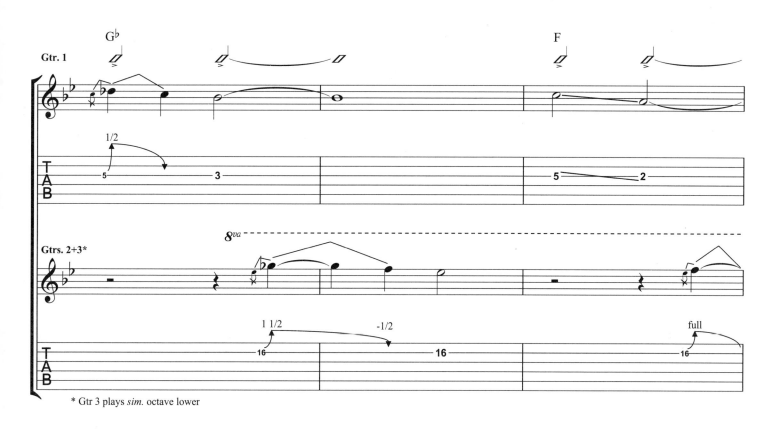

* Gtr 3 plays *sim.* octave lower

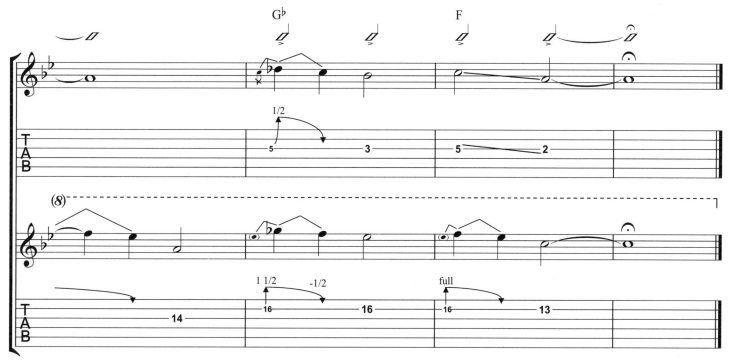

numb

Words & Music by
Chester Bennington, Mike Shinoda, Rob Bourdon, Joseph Hahn, Brad Delson & David Farrell

under the sur-face. I don't know what you're ex-pect-ing of me, put

Pre-chorus

under the pres-sure of walk-ing in your shoes. _(Caught in the un-der tow, just_

Gtr.2 (elec.)

mf let ring . . .
with clean tone + delay fx
Gtr. 1 *cont. sim*

caught in the un-der-tow.)

Ev-'ry step that I take is an-oth-er mis-take to you.

Chorus

G⁵

(Caught in the un-der-tow, just caught in the un--der-tow.)

I've be-come so

8va **All Gtrs.**

Harm.

p *ff* w/heavy dist.

Fig. 1

*tracked gtrs.

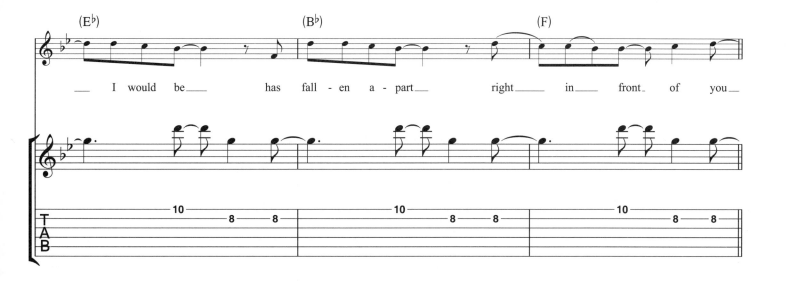

Pre-chorus

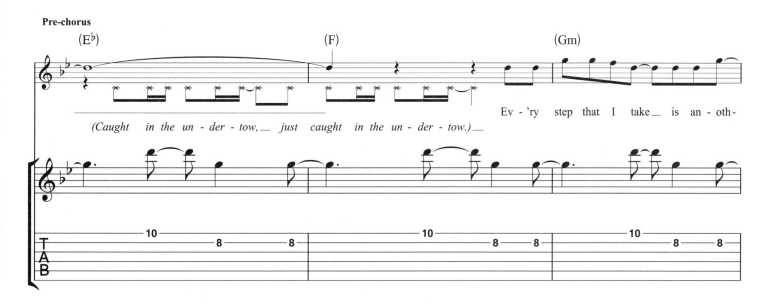

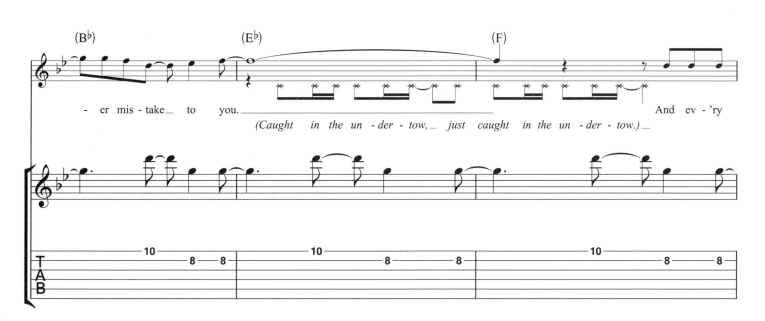

red morning light

Words & Music by Caleb Followill, Nathan Followill & Angelo Petraglia

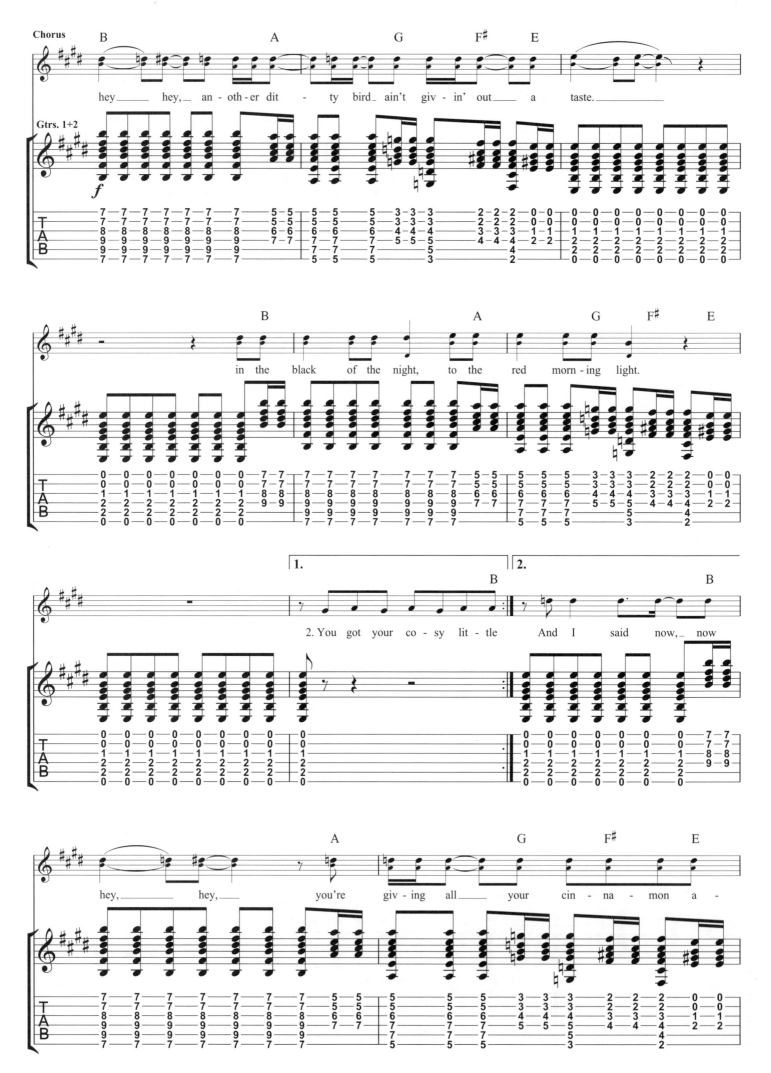

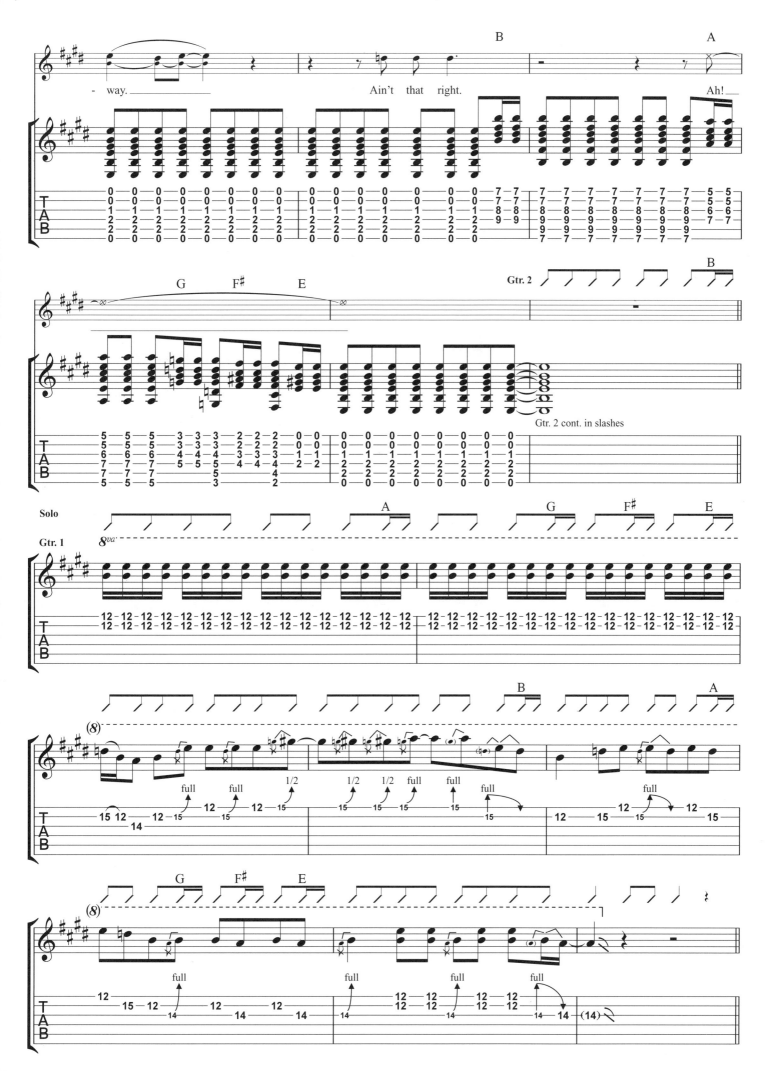

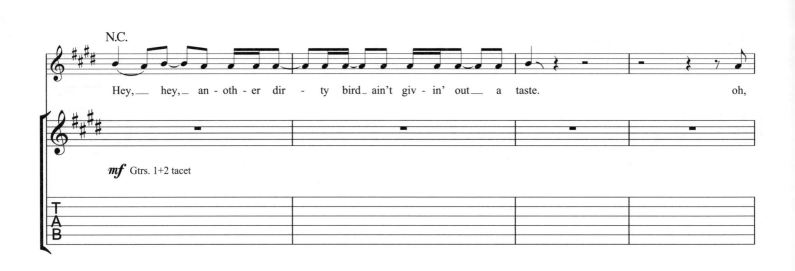

Hey,— hey,— an-oth-er dir - ty bird— ain't giv-in' out— a taste.   oh,

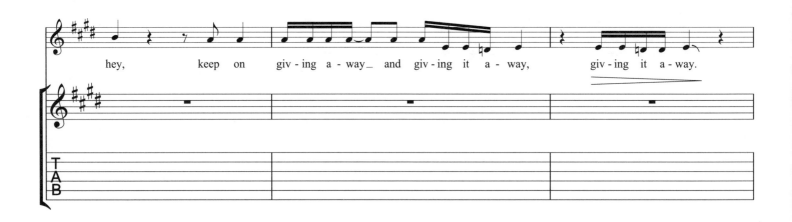

hey,   keep on giv-ing a - way— and giv-ing it a - way,   giv-ing it a - way.

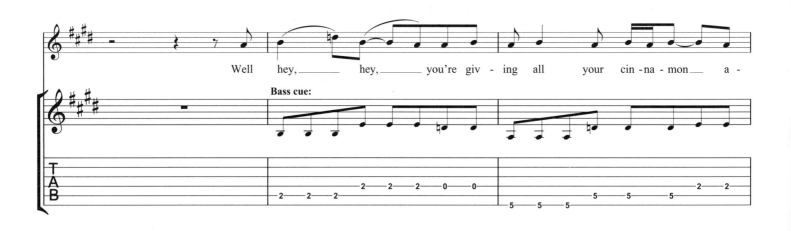

Well hey,———— hey,———— you're giv - ing all your cin-na-mon a -

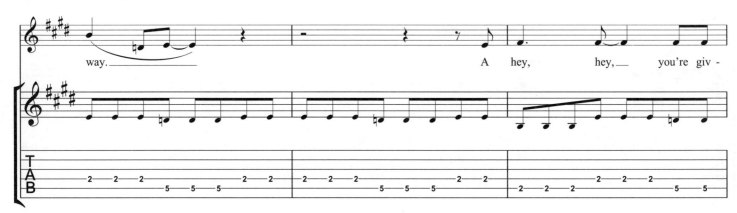

way.————————   A hey, hey,— you're giv -

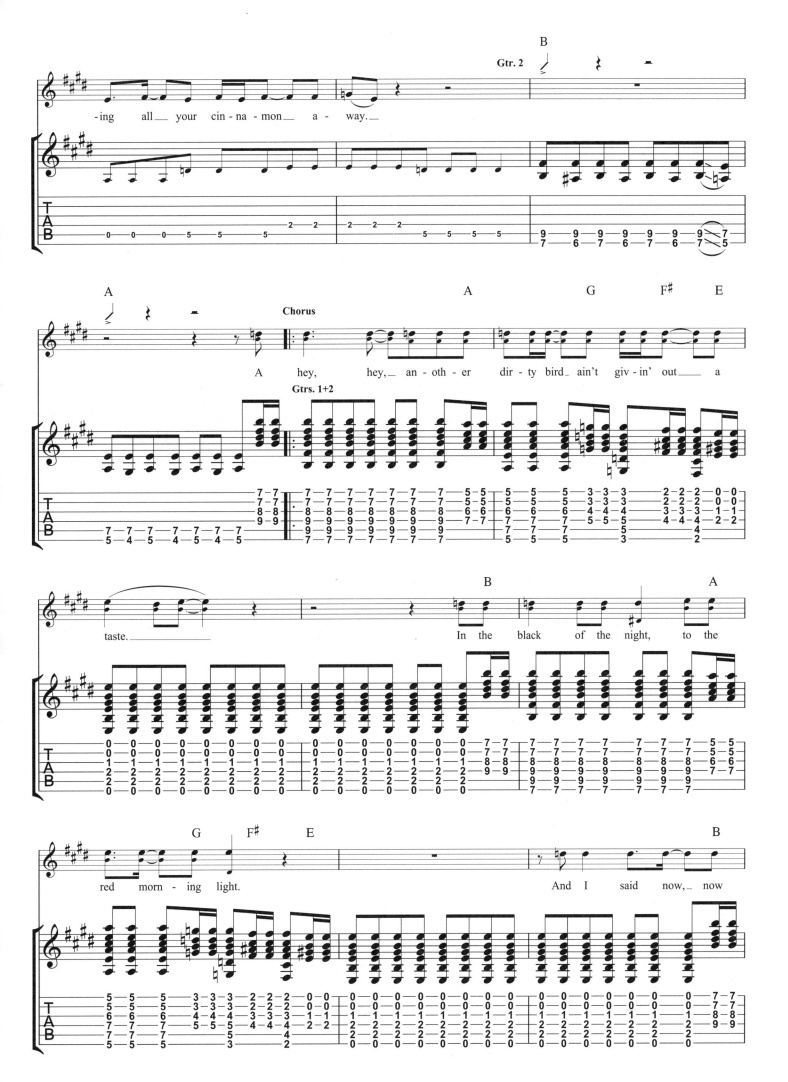

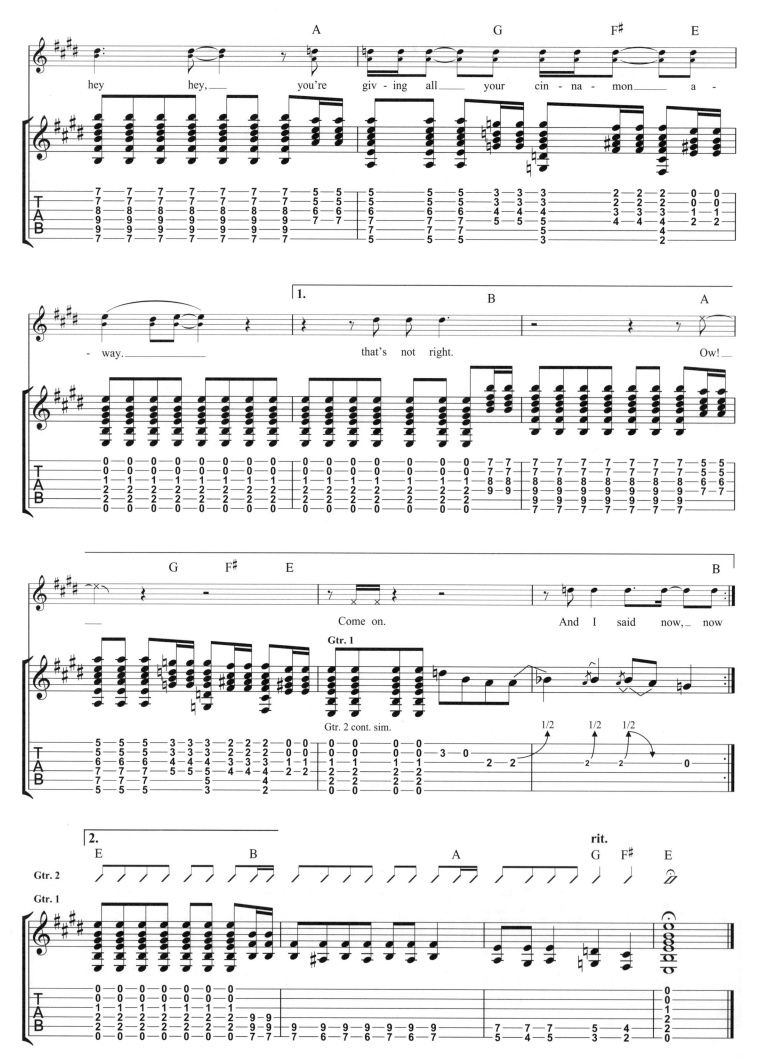

stumble and fall

Words & Music by Johnny Borrell & Björn Ågren

Gtr. 1 (No Capo)

Gtr. 2 (Capo 5th Fret)

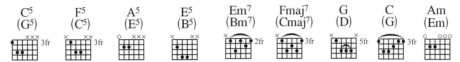

Intro

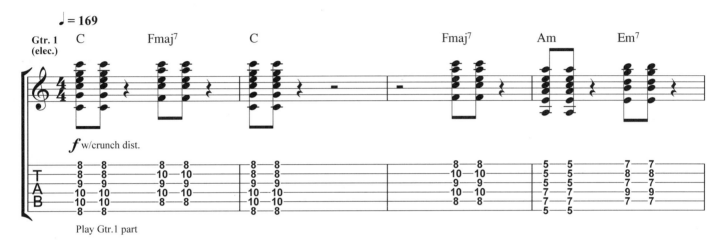

Play Gtr.1 part

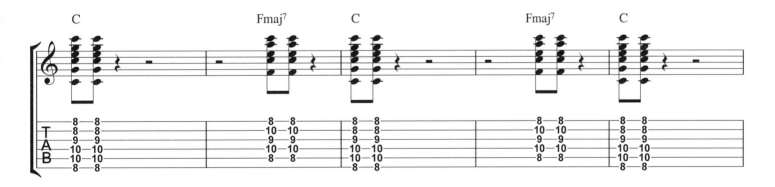

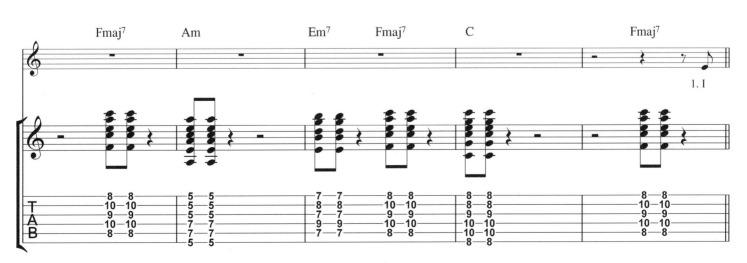

*Gtr. 2 chords. Symbols in parentheses represent chord names with respect to capoed Gtr. (TAB 0 = 5fr.)
Symbols above represent actual sounding chords.

110

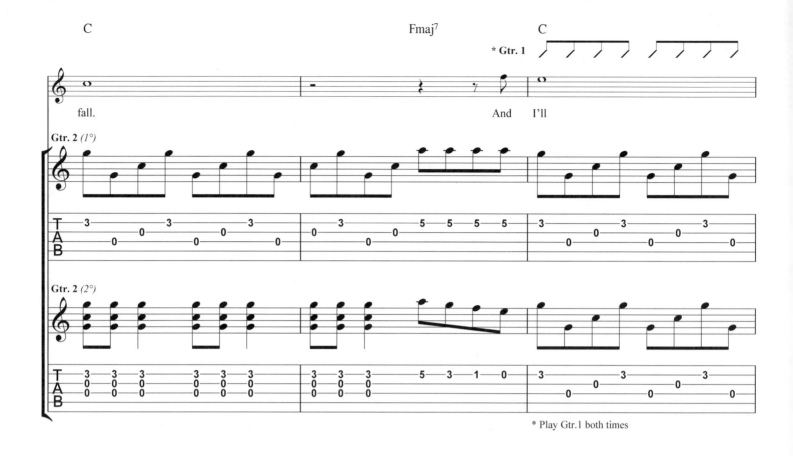

* Play Gtr.1 both times

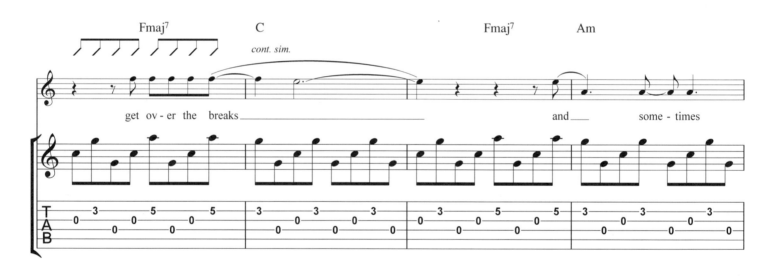

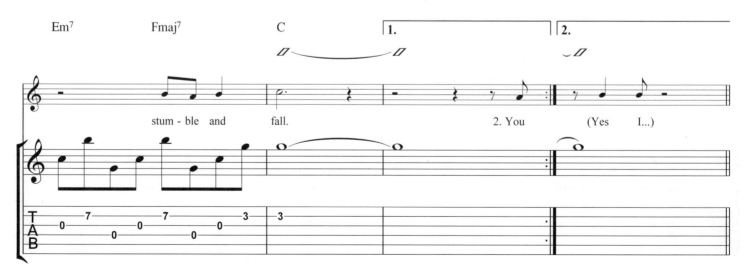

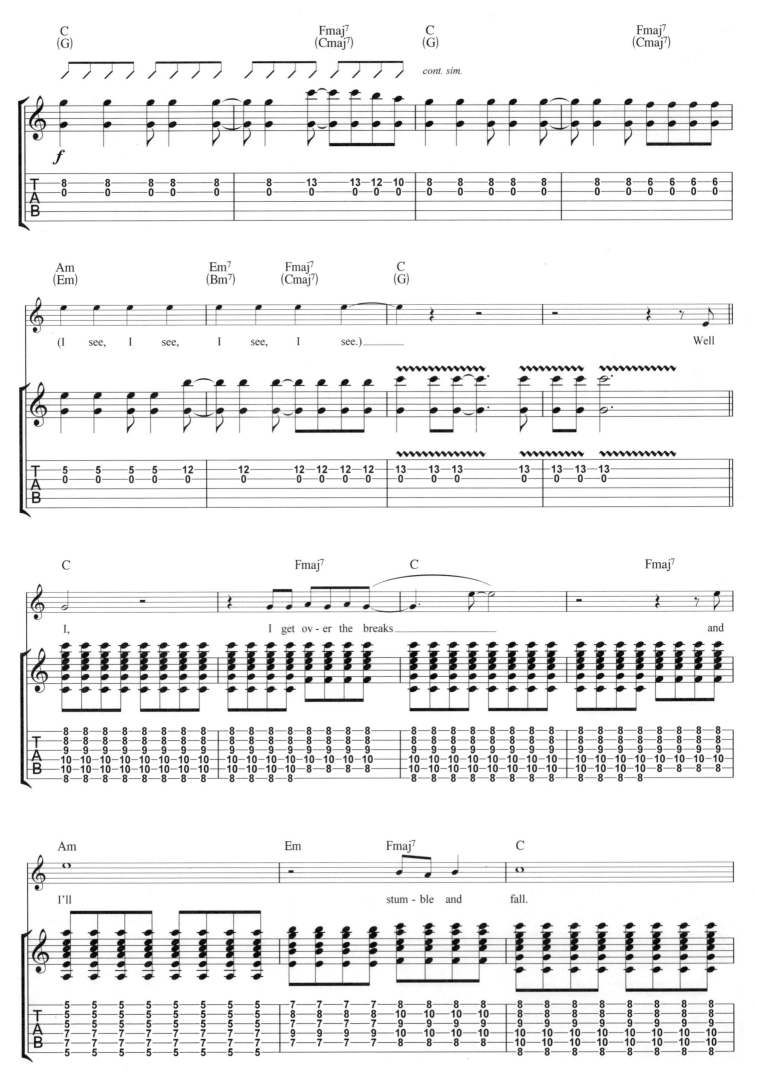

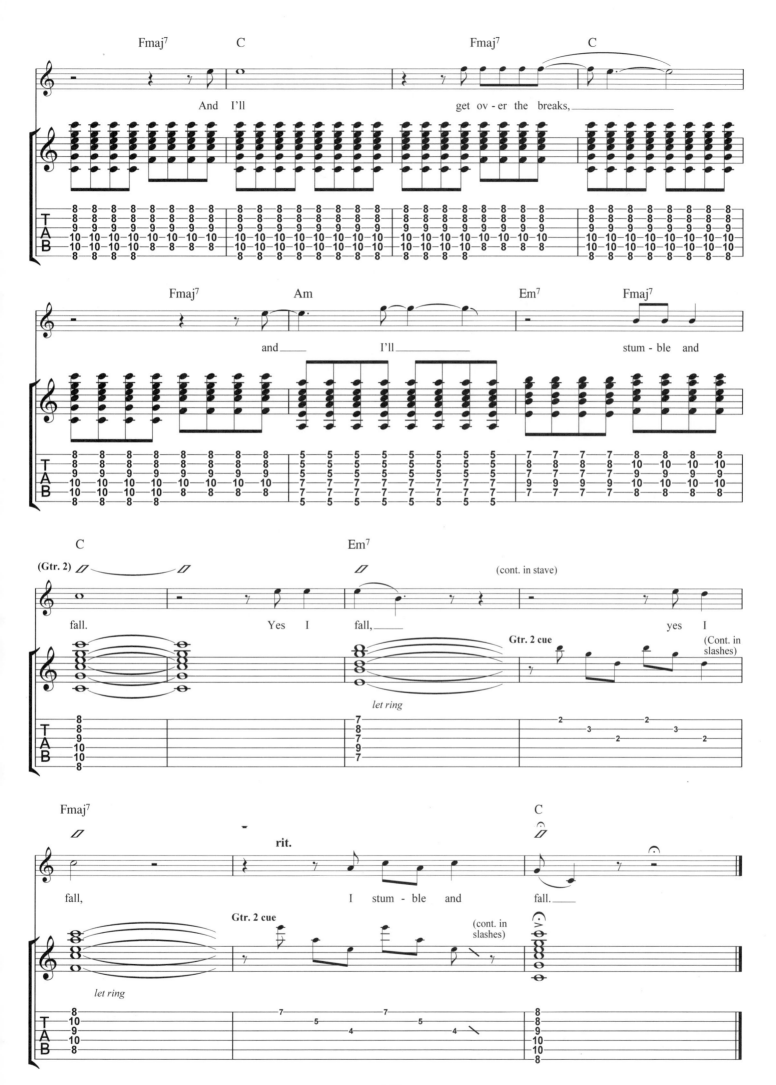

somebody told me

Words & Music by Brandon Flowers, Dave Keuning, Mark Stoermer & Ronnie Van Nucci

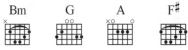

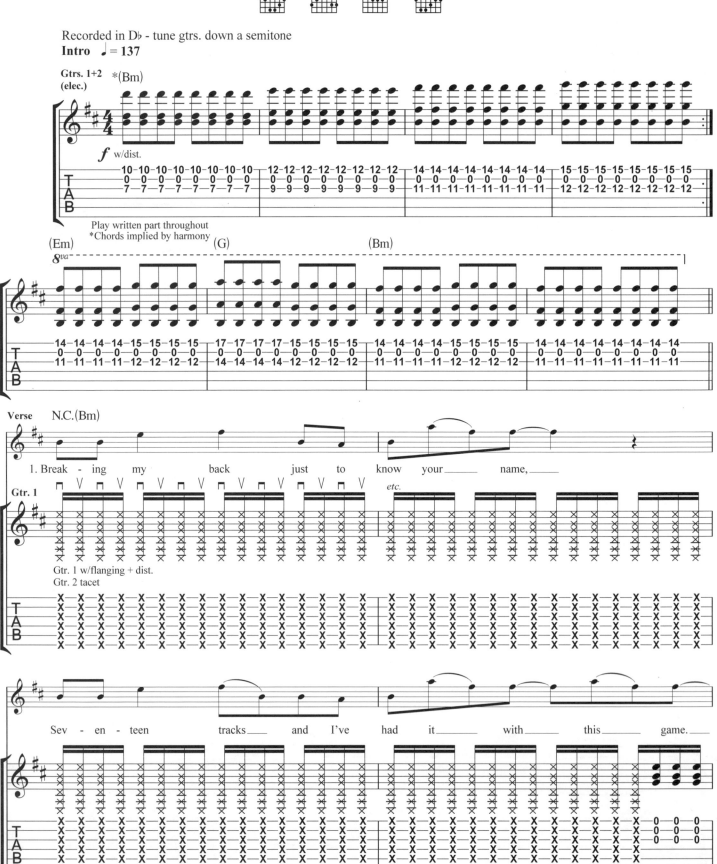

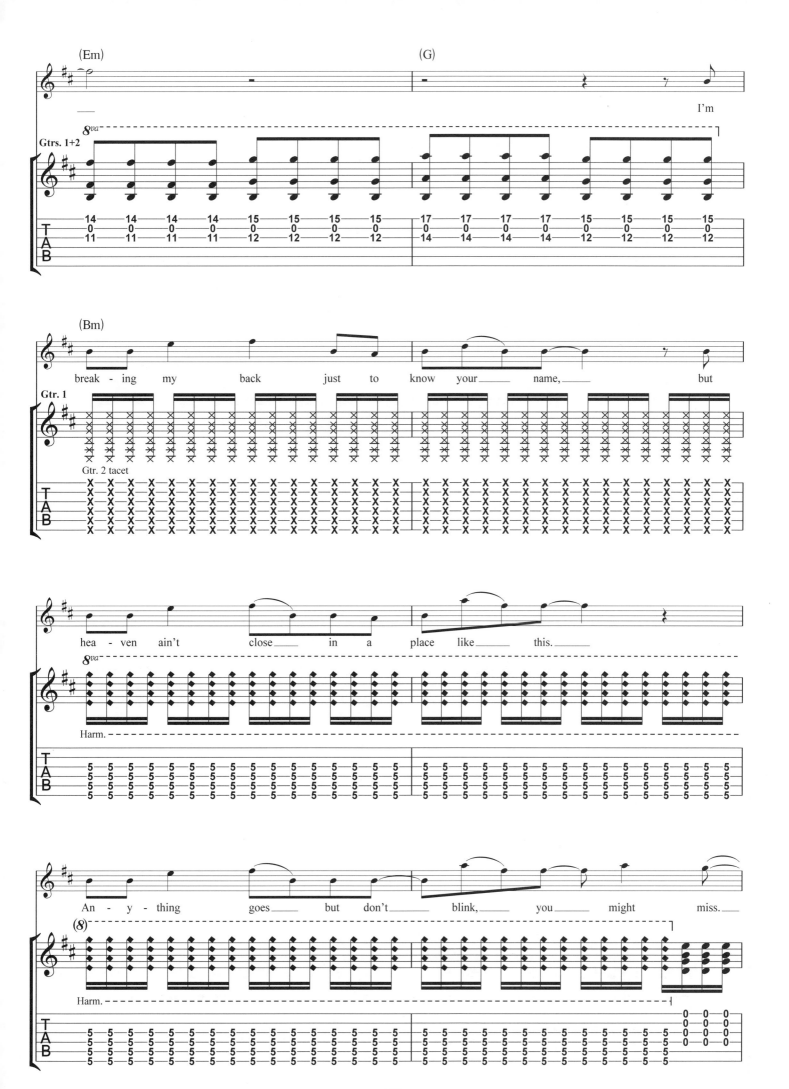

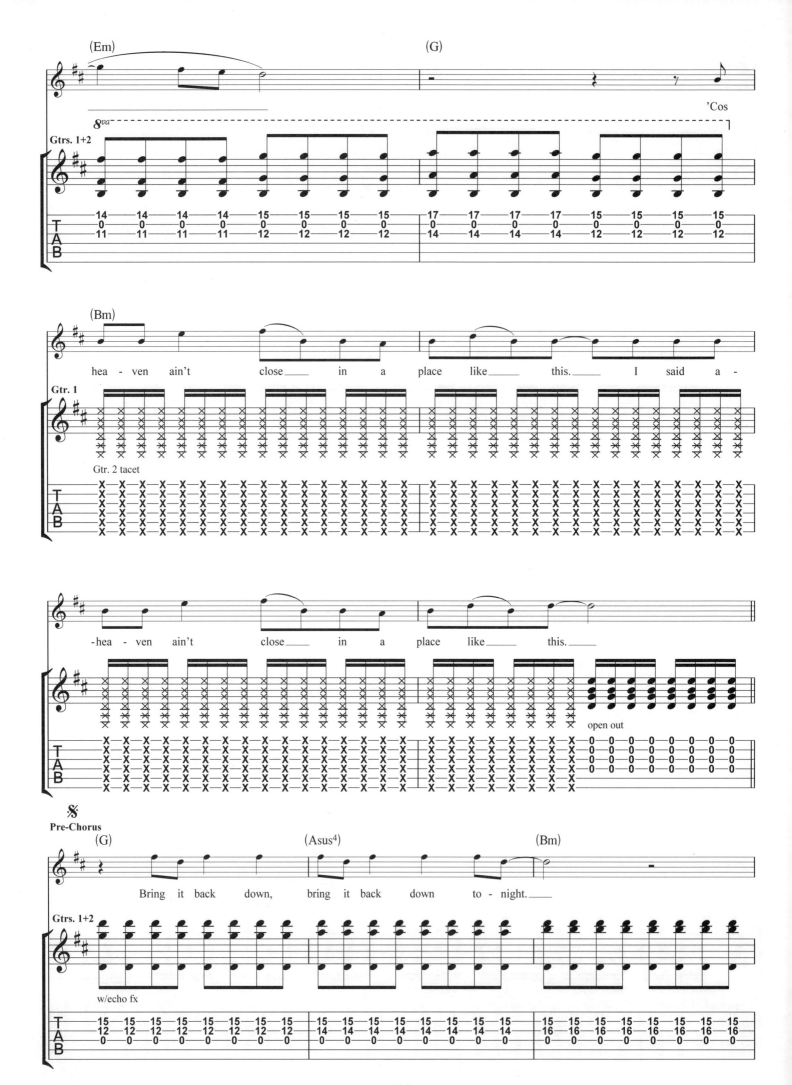

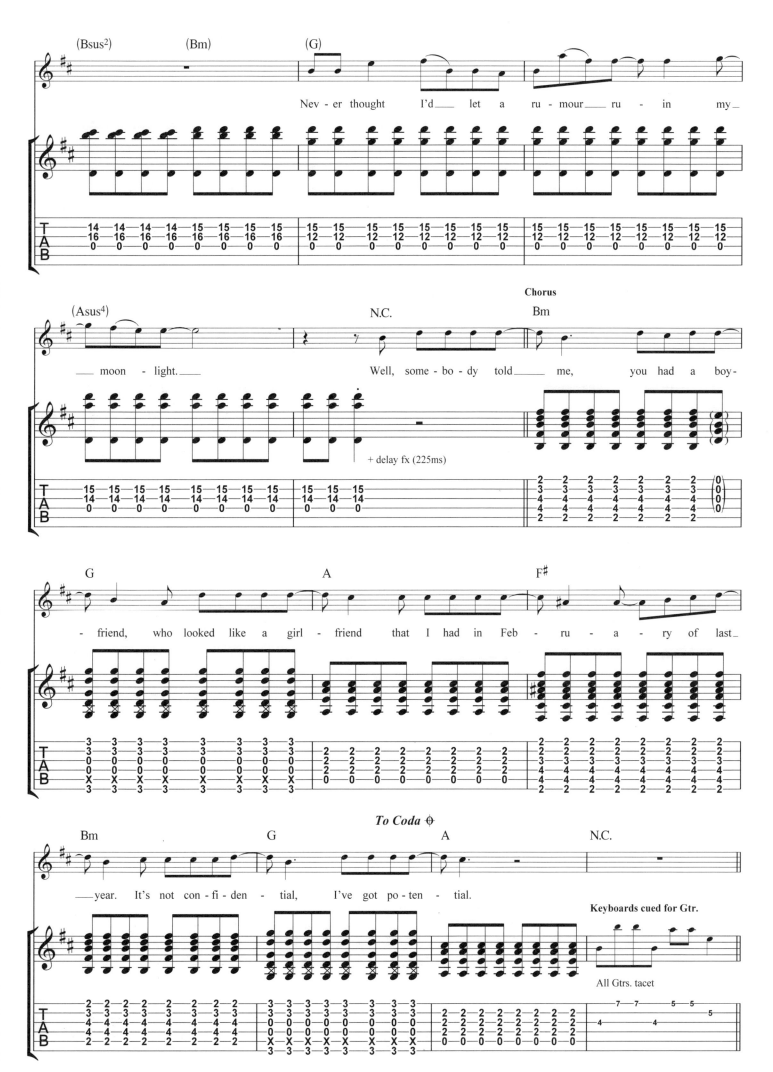

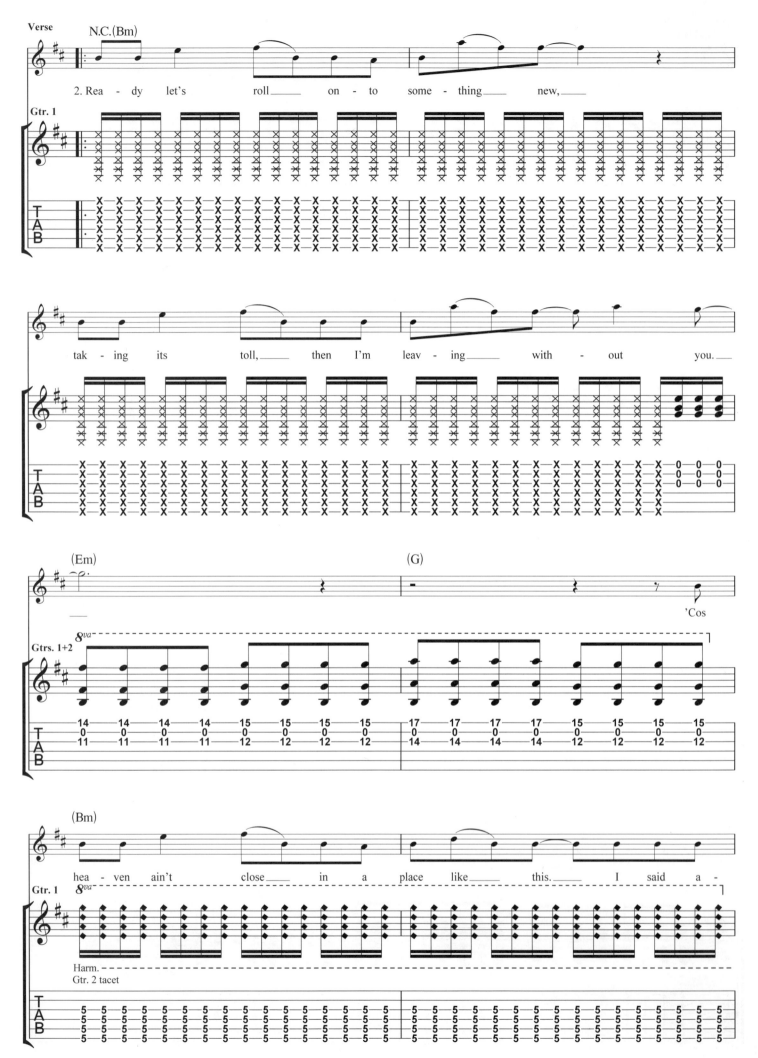

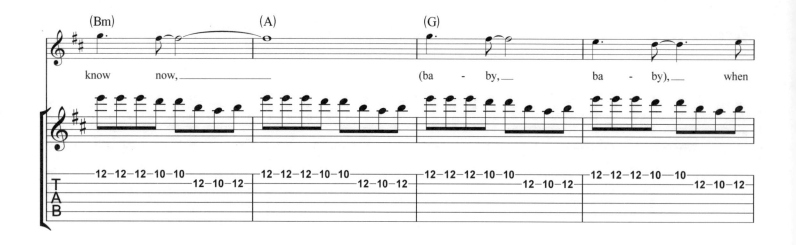

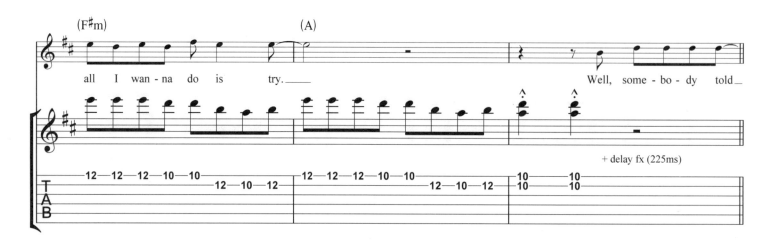

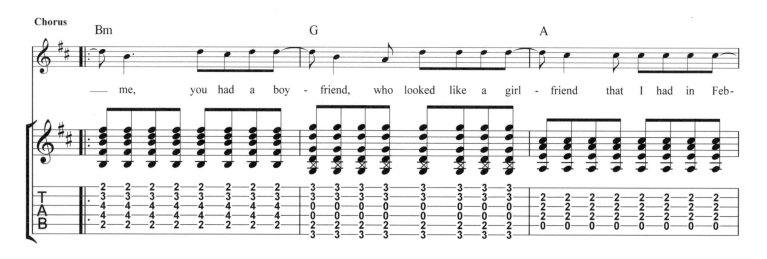

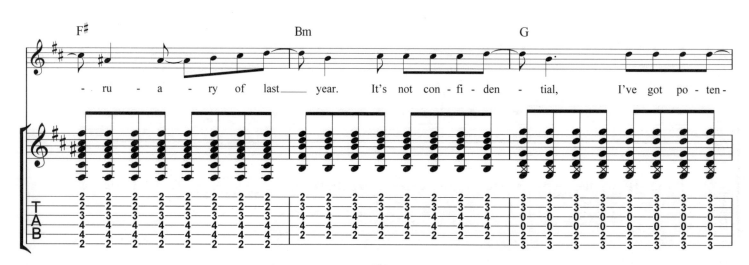

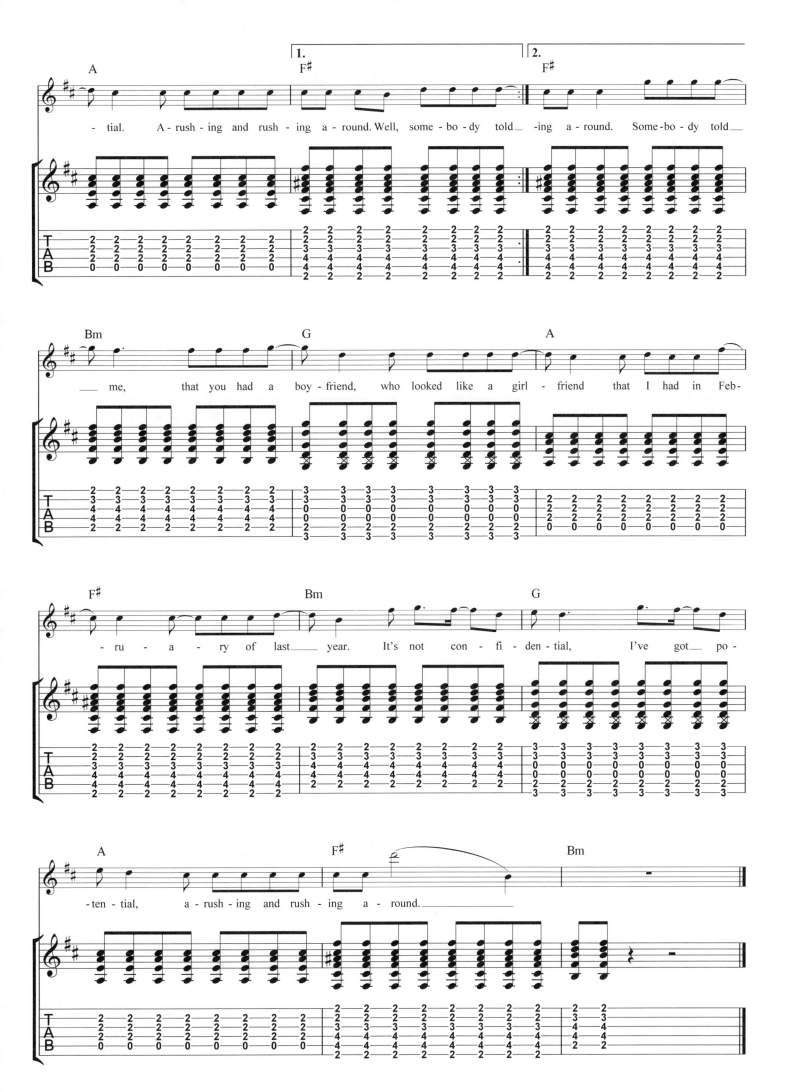

take me out

Words & Music by Alexander Kapranos & Nicholas McCarthy

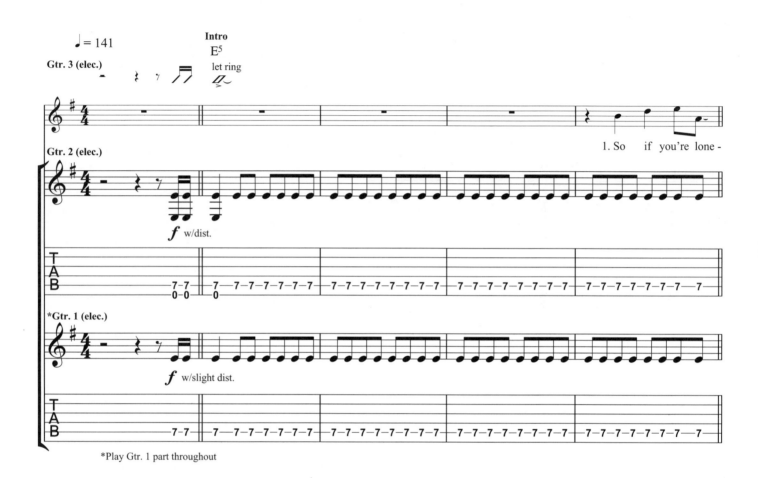

*Play Gtr. 1 part throughout

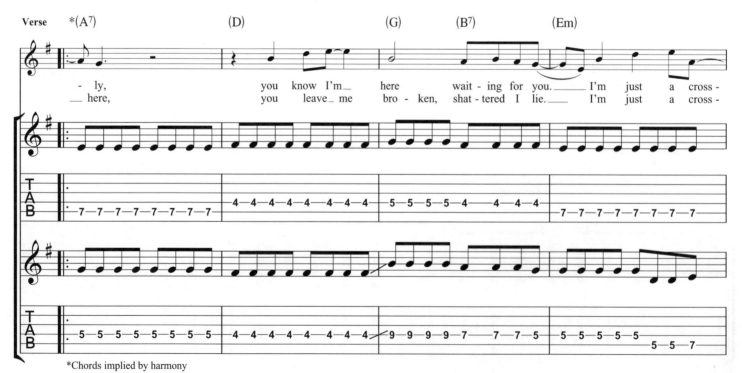

*Chords implied by harmony

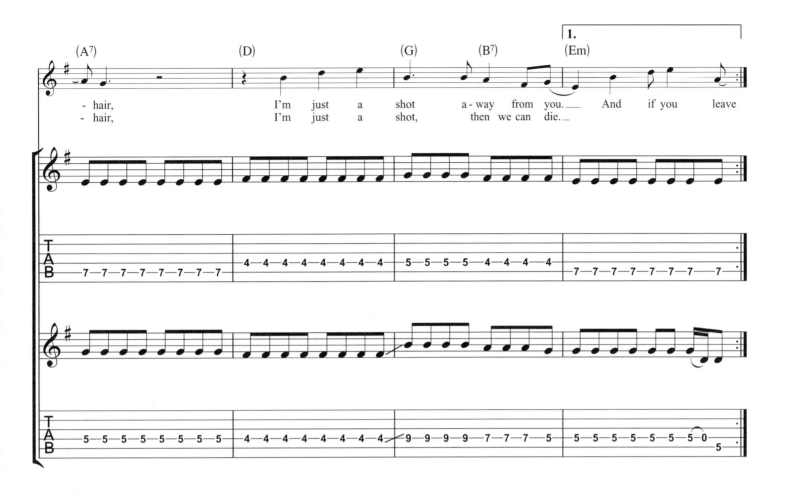

- hair,   I'm just a shot   a- way from you.__ And if you leave
- hair,   I'm just a shot,   then we can die.__

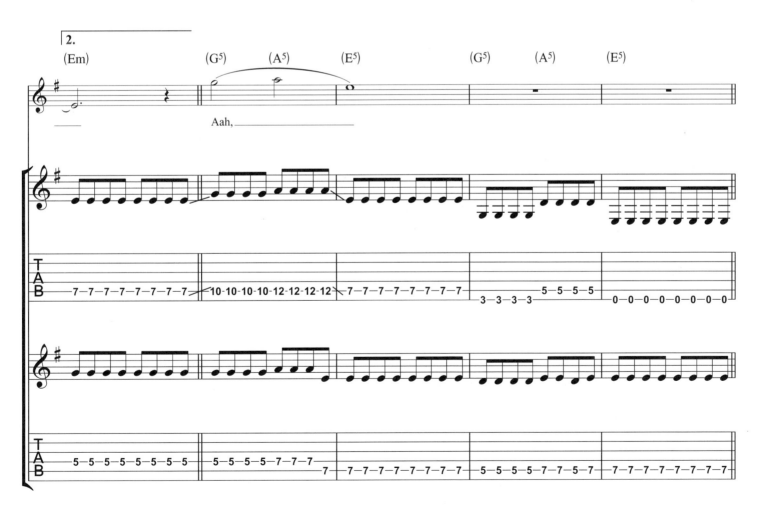

Aah,_____

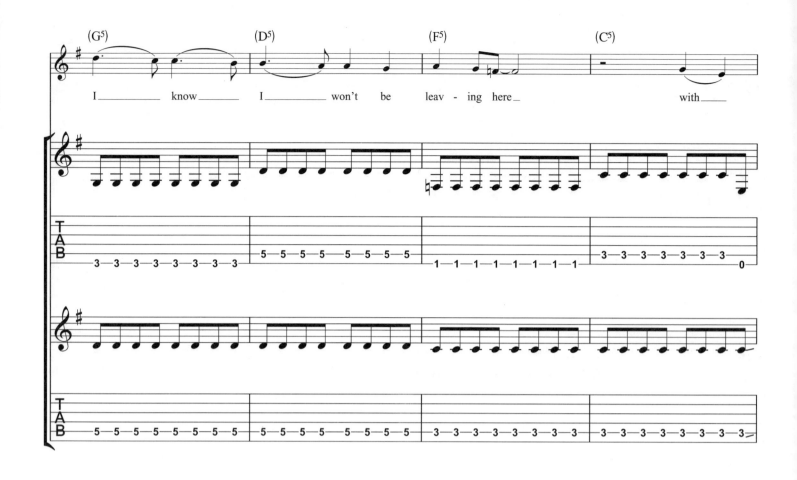

I_____ know_____ I_____ won't be leav - ing here___ with_____

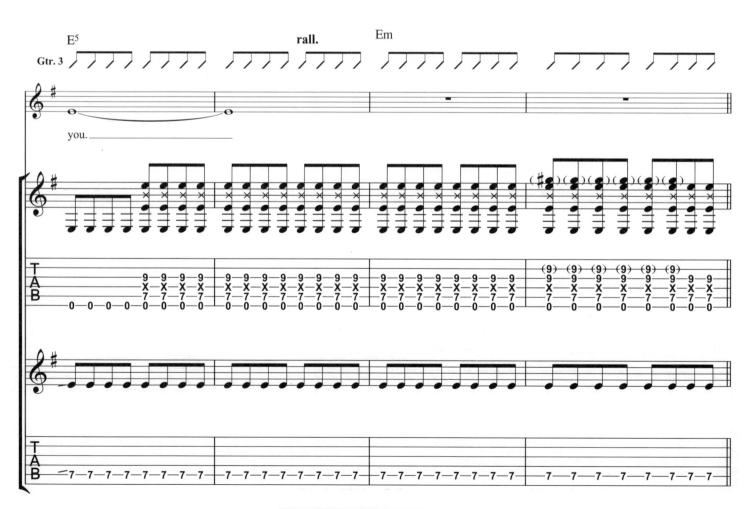

you._____

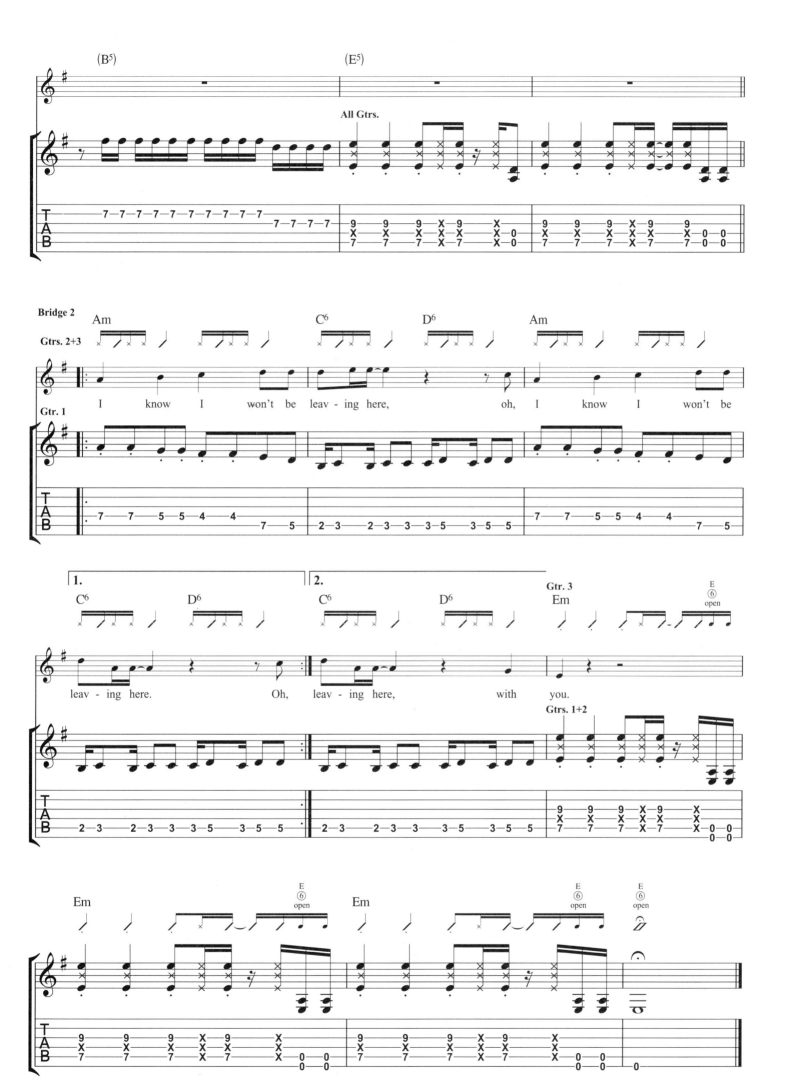

talk

Words & Music by Guy Berryman, Jon Buckland, Will Champion, Chris Martin, Ralf Hütter, Karl Bartoa & Emil Schult

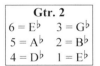

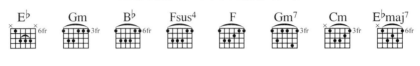

*w/reverb fx (1st 8 bars are cued)

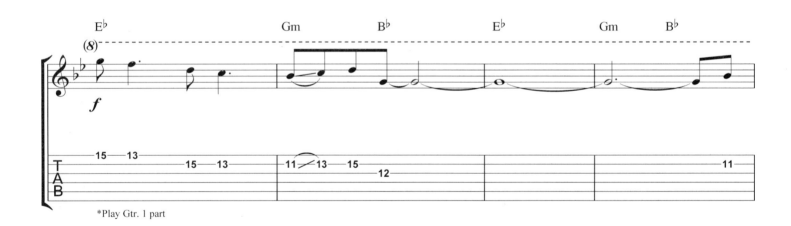

*Play Gtr. 1 part

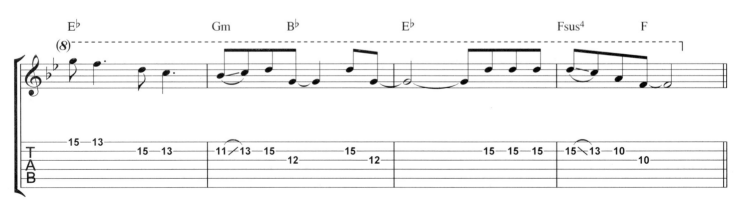

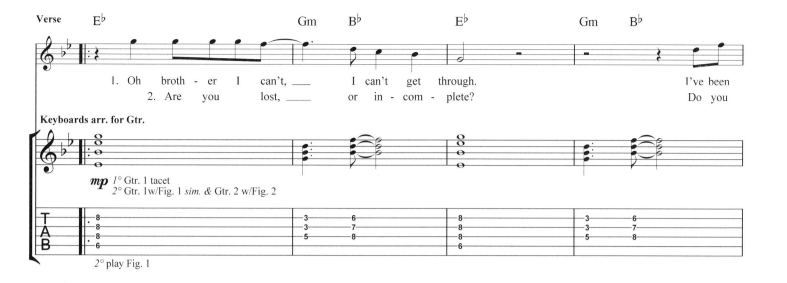

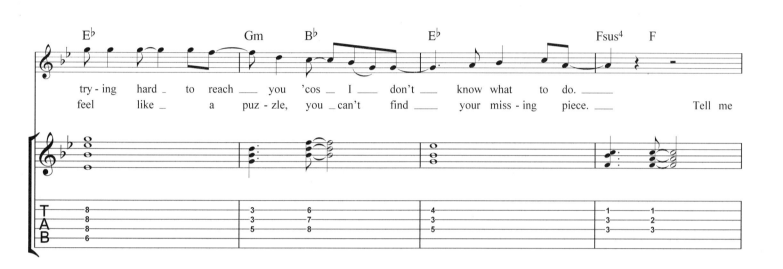

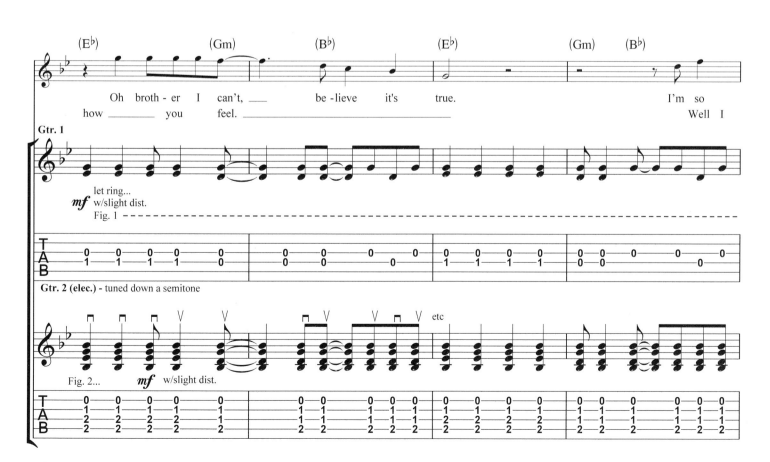

133

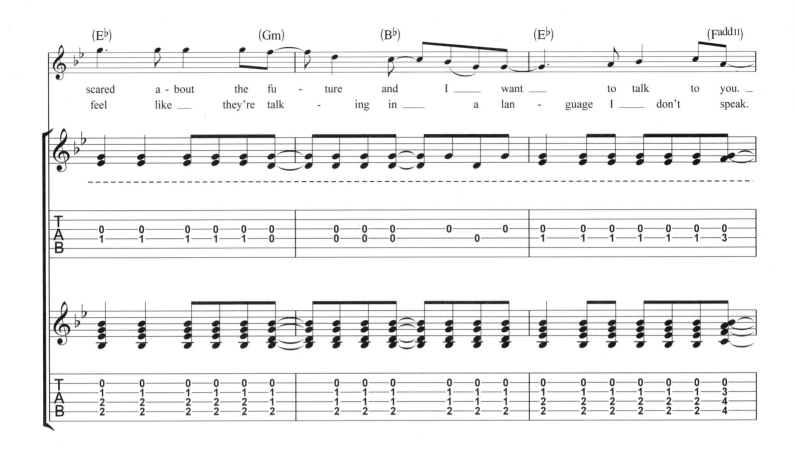

scared a - bout the fu - ture and I ____ want ____ to talk to you.
feel like ____ they're talk - ing in ____ a lan - guage I ____ don't speak.

Oh, I want ____ to talk to you. ____
And they're talk - ing it ____ to me. ____

...end Fig. 2

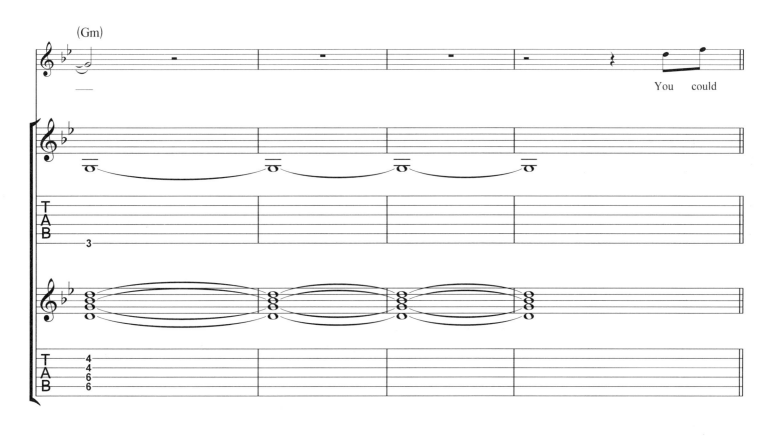

Chorus

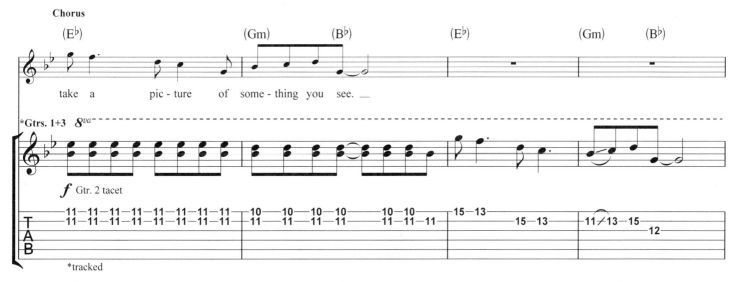

take a pic-ture of some-thing you see. __

*Gtrs. 1+3 8va

f Gtr. 2 tacet

*tracked

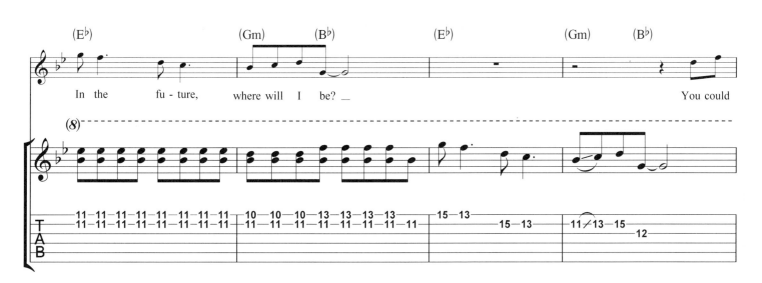

In the fu-ture, where will I be? __   You could

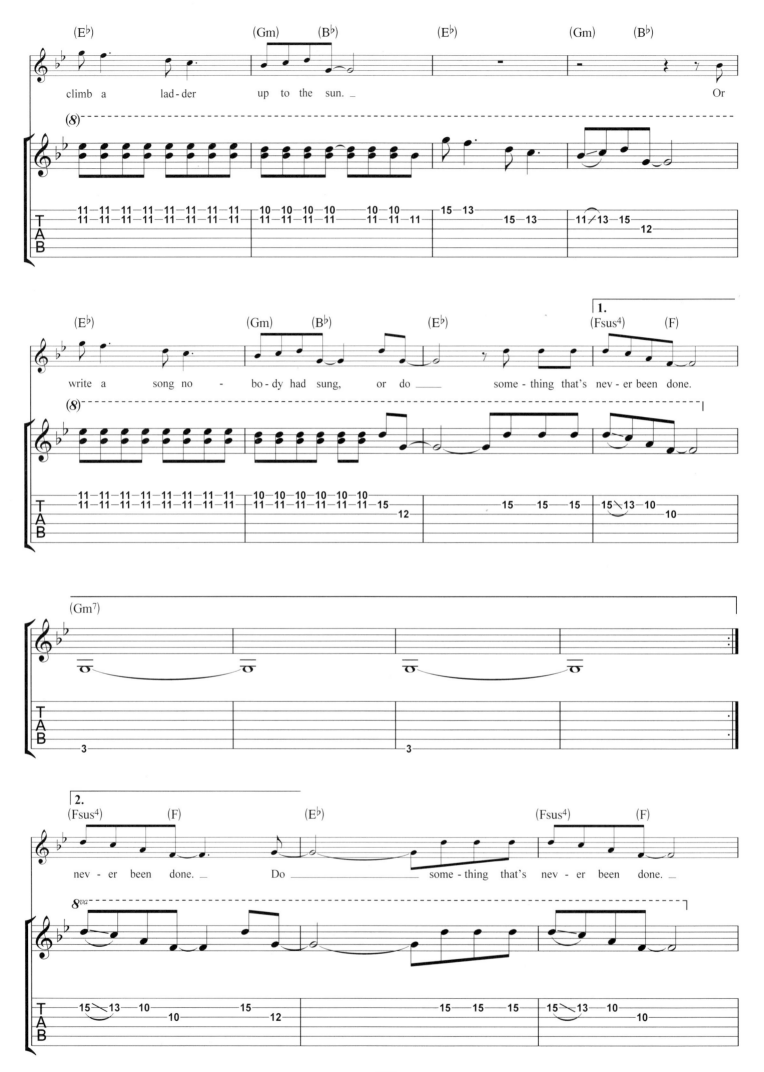

vegas two times

Words & Music by Kelly Jones

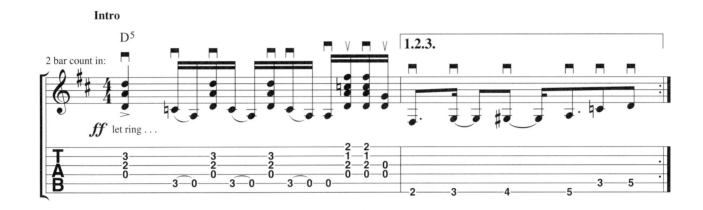

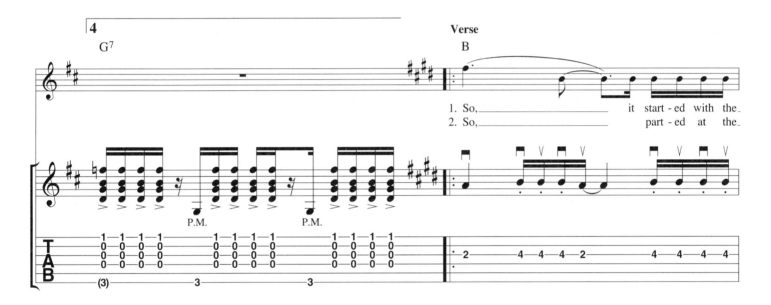

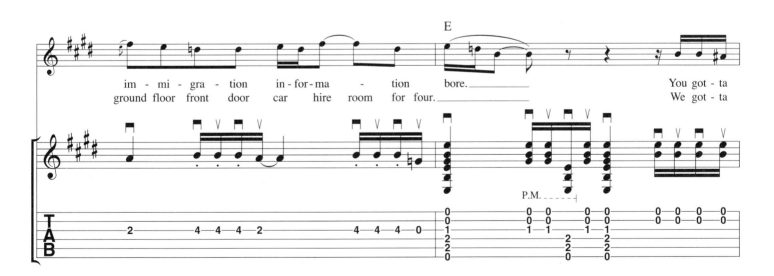

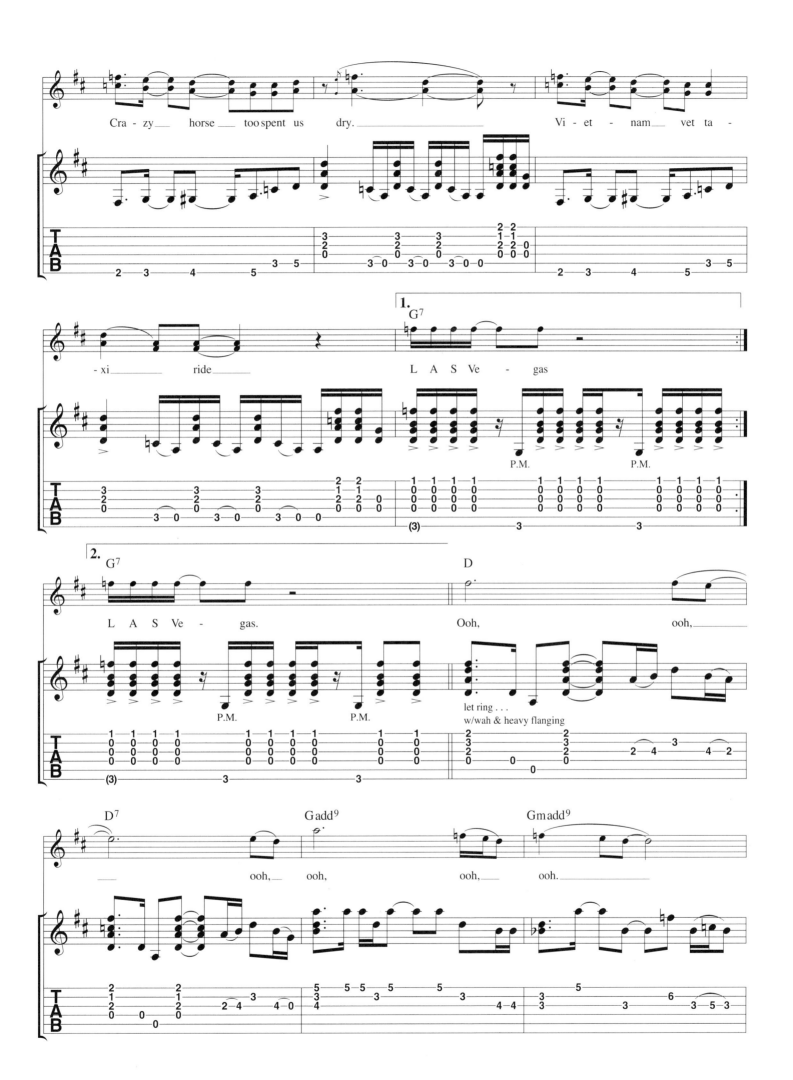

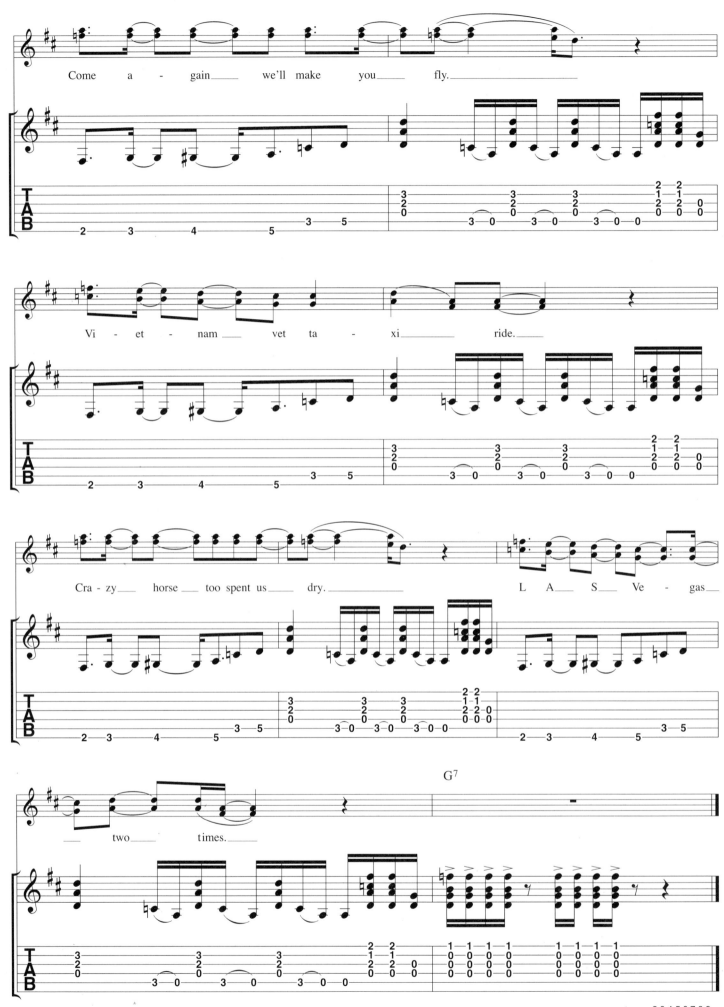

Come a - gain___ we'll make you___ fly.___

Vi - et - nam ___ vet ta - xi___ ride.___

Cra - zy___ horse___ too spent us___ dry._____ L A___ S ___ Ve - gas___

G⁷

___ two___ times.___